## *It's another Quality Book from CGP*

*This book is for anyone doing GCSE Double Science at Higher Level.*

*It contains lots of tricky questions designed to make you sweat — because that's the only way you'll get any better.*

*It's also got some daft bits in to try and make the whole experience at least vaguely entertaining for you.*

## *What CGP is all about*

*Our sole aim here at CGP is to produce the highest quality books — carefully written, immaculately presented and dangerously close to being funny.*

*Then we work our socks off to get them out to you — at the cheapest possible prices.*

# Contents




Published by Coordination Group Publications Ltd.

Coordinated by Paddy Gannon

*Contributors:*
Bill Dolling, Jane Cartwright, Alex Kizildas

Design Editor: Ed Lacey. With thanks to Colin Wells for the proofreading

*Updated by:*
Chris Dennett, James Paul Wallis, Dominic Hall, Katherine Reed, Suzanne Worthington

ISBN 1 84146 405 8

Groovy website: www.cgpbooks.co.uk

Printed by Elanders Hindson, Newcastle upon Tyne.

# Current, Voltage, Resistance

*These questions are about electric current: what it is, what makes it move and what tries to stop it.*

**Q1** **Fill the gaps** in the following paragraph about electric current.
Words to use: *electrons, charged, positive, metal, circuit*

Current is a flow of __________ particles around a __________ .
Electric current can only flow if there are free __________ like in a __________,
where electrons flow throughout the structure of __________ ions.

**Q2** **Copy** the circuit diagram and mark on the (+) and (–) on the cell.
**Mark** the direction of the current, ⟶, and the direction of the moving electrons, ·········· .

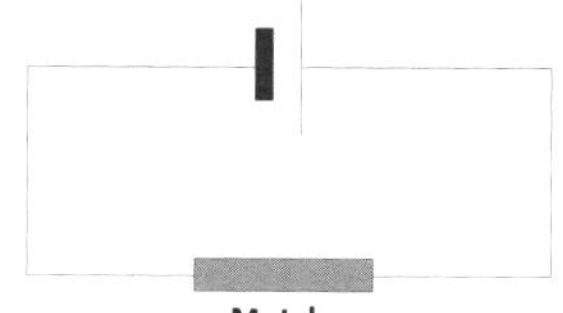


**Q3** **Copy** these sentences using the correct underlined words.

The <u>current / voltage / resistance</u> in a circuit flows from <u>positive / negative</u> to <u>positive / negative</u>.
Electrons flow in the <u>same direction as / opposite direction to</u> the flow of "conventional current".

**Q4** **Copy the diagram** on the right.
**Label** the electrodes positive (+) and negative (–) .
**Draw arrows** to show the movement of ions (⊕⟶, ⟵⊖).

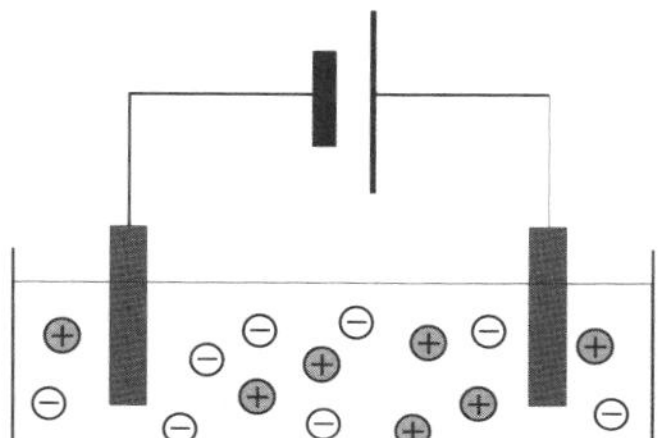

**Q5** **Copy and complete** the following paragraph about electrolysis.
Use these words: sodium chloride, sodium chloride solution, liquids, positive, negative, charged particles, dissolved

Electrolytes are __________ which contain freely moving __________. They are either ions __________ in water like __________ or molten ionic liquids like __________. When the current is switched on, the __________ ions move towards the positive electrode and the __________ ions move towards the negative electrode.

Resistance is anything that reduces the current in a circuit. Electrical components and household electrical appliances all have some resistance.

**Q6** A kettle is plugged into a 230V mains socket.
There is a current of 10A in its element.
**Calculate** the resistance of the element.

**Q7** Find the current in a resistor of 18Ω when it is connected to a 9V battery.

**Q8** Complete the table on the right:

| Voltage(V) | Current(A) | Resistance(Ω) |
|---|---|---|
| | 2.0 | 6.0 |
| 230 | | 23.0 |
| 6 | 3.0 | |
| 1.5 | | 15.0 |
| 12 | 4.0 | |
| | 1.5 | 5.0 |

**Q9** *The table shows measurements of voltage across and current in a component.*

a) **Plot a graph** of voltage (volts) against current (amps).
b) **Find** the component's resistance.
c) Is the component a resistor, a filament lamp or a diode?
d) **Explain** your answer to part **c**).

| Voltage(V) | Current(A) |
|---|---|
| 0 | 0 |
| 0.75 | 1.0 |
| 1.50 | 2.0 |
| 2.25 | 3.0 |
| 3.00 | 4.0 |
| 3.75 | 5.0 |

# Current, Voltage, Resistance

**Q10** Answer the questions for the circuits **a)** to **f)**.

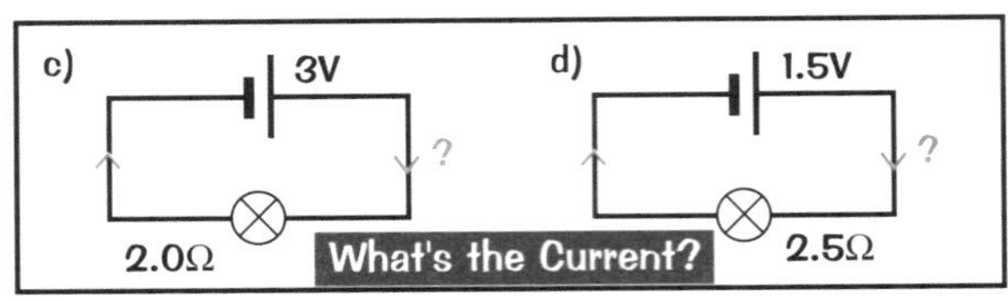


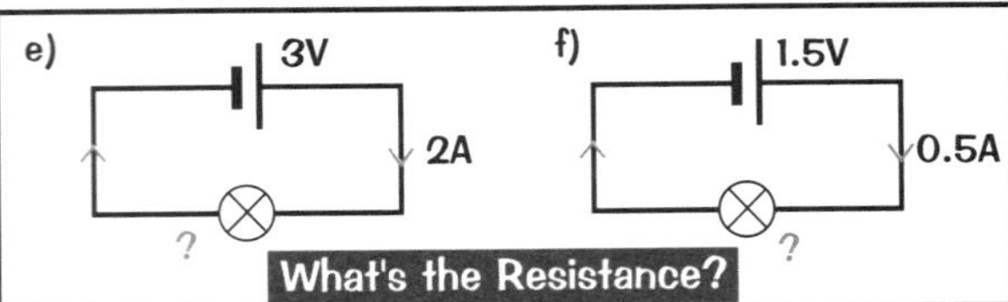


**Q11** Fill in the gaps (or circle) the correct answer:

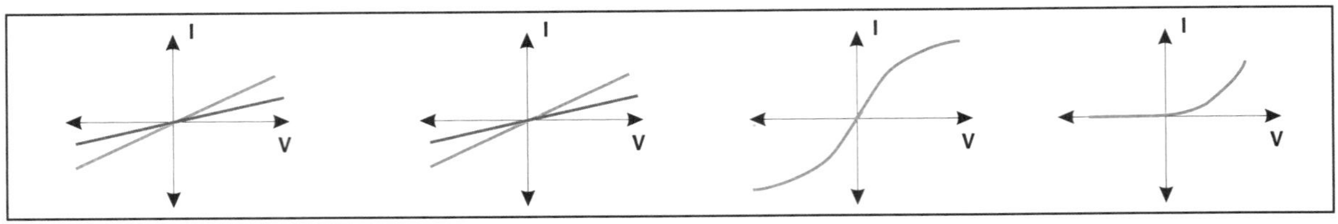


LONG AND SHORT WIRE
The graph with the steeper slope is the **longer/shorter** wire of the same material as it has a **higher/ lower** resistance.

THIN AND THICK WIRE
The graph with the steeper slope is the **thick/thin** wire of the same material as it has a **higher/lower** resistance.

FILAMENT LAMP
As the ____________ of the filament ____________, the resistance increases.

DIODE
Current in a diode can only be in ______ ____________.

**Q12** Match the words with their correct description on the right:

a) current
b) resistance
c) coulomb
d) diode
e) watt (W)
f) electrolyte
g) voltage increase
h) amp (A)
i) ammeter
j) nichrome
k) voltmeter
l) increase the resistance
m) copper
n) volt (V)

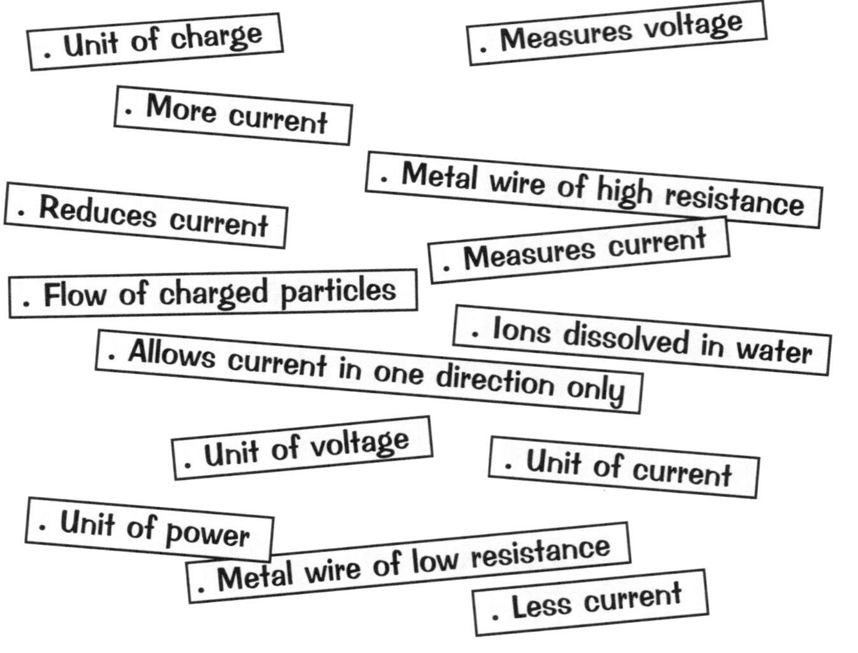


## Top Tips

You need to understand **what electricity is**, **what makes it move** and **what tries** to stop it, otherwise you won't understand any of the questions about electricity in this section. You do need to **learn** the four graphs of current/voltage in question 11. They come up in the Exam pretty often.

# Circuit Symbols and Devices

**Q1** **Complete the table** for these electrical components. You need to know these for your exam.

| CIRCUIT SYMBOL | NAME FOR CIRCUIT SYMBOL | WHAT IT DOES |
|---|---|---|
| | | |
| | LDR | |
| | | Converts electrical energy into sound energy. |
| V | | |
| | | Wire inside it breaks if the current is too high, protecting the appliance. |
| | | |
| | Thermistor | |
| | Open Switch | |
| | | Allows current in one direction only |
| | | Adjusted to alter the current in a circuit |
| M | | |
| | Ammeter | |

**Q2 a)** **Design a circuit** using these electrical components that would allow the speed of the motor to be varied.

**b)** *The variable resistor can be adjusted to slow the motor down.* **Explain** this using the words **resistance** and **current**.

**c)** When the motor is **slowed down**, what happens to the reading on the ammeter?

**d)** **Suggest** how you could slow down the motor even more by changing one of the components.

**Q3** *A dimmer switch controls the brightness of a light: turn it clockwise to increase the brightness, or anti-clockwise to decrease it. It works by using a variable resistor to control the current in the bulb.*

— It is illustrated in the diagram opposite.

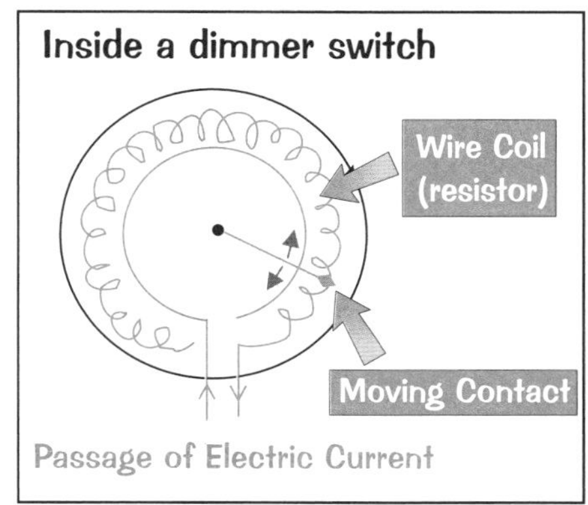


**a)** Draw the path followed by the current if the lights are **dim**; **medium brightness**; and **bright**.

Below are three readings of current and resistance taken from the switch at different settings.

**b)** Complete the table using the same descriptions for brightness used in part **a)**.

**c)** What happens to the size of the current when the resistance is increased?

**d)** What happens to the size of the current when the resistance is decreased?

| Brightness of Lights | Current(A) | Resistance(Ω) |
|---|---|---|
| | 1.0 | 6.0 |
| | 2.0 | 3.0 |
| | 3.0 | 2.0 |

# More Devices

**Q1** Draw a **circuit diagram** of a battery-operated torch, with 2 cells, a switch and a filament bulb.

**Q2** Draw a circuit diagram of a **loudspeaker**, with an a.c. supply and a switch.

**Q3** Draw a circuit diagram of an **electric heater**, a d.c. power supply and switch.

**Q4** Draw a circuit diagram of an **intruder alarm**, with an on/off switch, a hidden switch which is triggered when trodden on, and a **loudspeaker**, all driven by an a.c. power supply.
— Now draw the circuit for a similar alarm which is triggered by light.

**Q5** **Use the data** in the table opposite to plot a graph of resistance R, against light intensity. **Draw** the best fit curve.

| Resistance / Ω | Light Intensity / units |
|---|---|
| 100,000 | 0.5 |
| 55,000 | 2.0 |
| 40,000 | 3.0 |
| 20,000 | 5.0 |
| 1000 | 7.5 |
| 100 | 10.0 |

**a)** How does the resistance change as the light gets brighter?

**b)** How does the resistance change as the light gets dimmer?

**c)** Looking at the **slope** of the graph, describe how the resistance changes in bright light compared to dim light, as the light gets brighter.

**d)** Give **two uses** for LDRs and **explain** how one of them works (drawing the circuit diagram may help).

**Q6** The graph below shows how the resistance of a thermistor changes with temperature.

**a)** Write a sentence to **describe** what happens to the resistance of the thermistor as the temperature changes.

**b)** What is the resistance at 25°C (approximately)?

**c)** Give an example of where a thermistor is used as a **temperature sensor**.

**d)** What **change in temperature** increases the resistance from 90Ω to 130Ω?

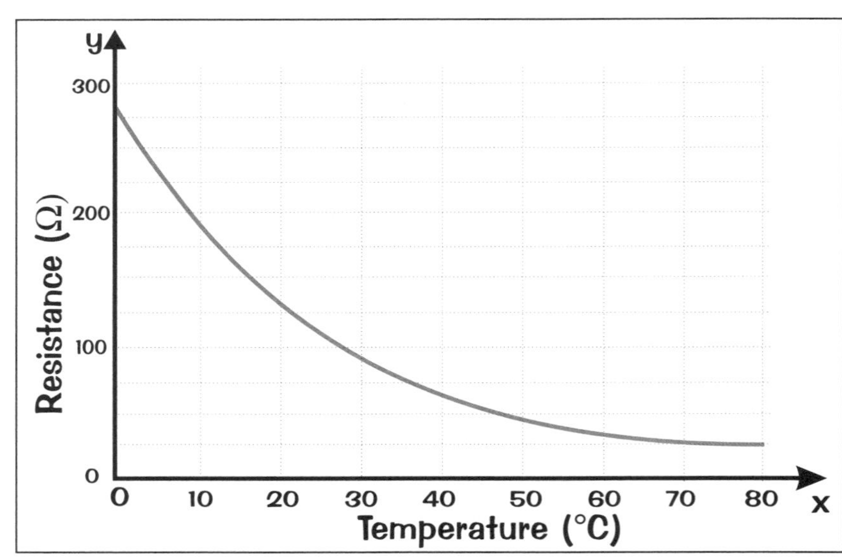


## Top Tips

There is usually a clue in the symbol, too — a motor has a capital M, a diode has a little arrow telling you which way the current can go. Look out for the five "special" components — variable resistor, diode, light emitting diode (LED), light dependent resistor (LDR) and thermistor.

# Series Circuits

Electrical devices can have dramatically different effects if they are arranged in series or parallel, as you know. The next four pages test if you know the rules for both types of circuits.

**Use a pencil and ruler when drawing circuit diagrams so that they're clear, or else you'll only get half marks!**

**Q1** **Draw** a circuit diagram of a 6V battery, a switch and two lamps in series.

**Q2** **Draw** a circuit diagram of a 12V power supply with a fuse and a heater in series.

**Q3** The circuit below shows two lamps. Initially these lamps are of **normal brightness**. Work out the brightness of the lamp(s) when the following modifications **a)** to **f)** are carried out.

— Choose from: **off**, **dimmer**, **normal** or **brighter**.

- **a)** One lamp is unscrewed.
- **b)** One cell is turned around.
- **c)** Another cell is added the same way around as the others.
- **d)** Another cell is added the other way around to the others.
- **e)** Another bulb is added.
- **f)** Both cells are turned around.

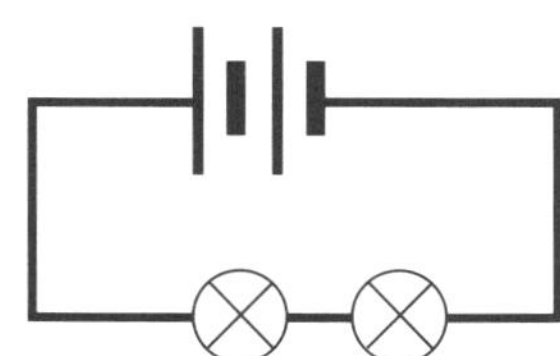

**Q4** Draw a circuit with a 2Ω and 4Ω resistor in series with a 6V battery.

- **a)** What is the total resistance?
- **b)** Calculate the current in the circuit.

**Q5** The resistances of the resistors in this circuit are equal. What are they if the ammeter reads 1A?

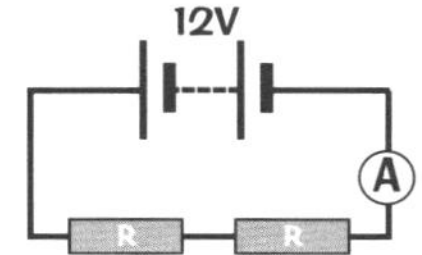


**Q6** Christmas tree lights are a shining example of lamps in **series**. What happens if one of the lamps is removed?

Find the **total resistance** of 10 lamps running off the mains (240V), if the current in each lamp is 0.5A. What is the resistance of each lamp?

**Q7** Match each series combination **a)** → **d)** with the equivalent single resistor **1)** → **4)**.

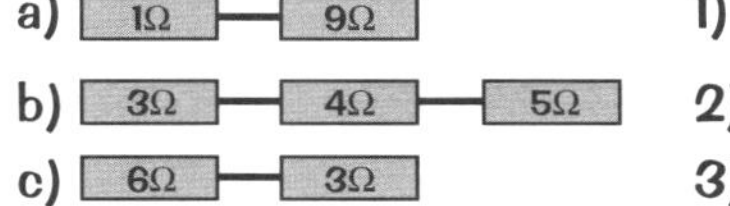


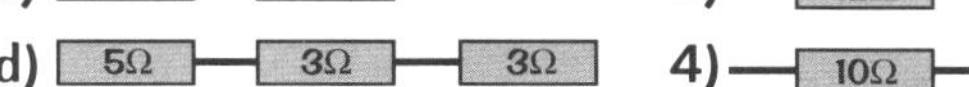


**Q8** **a)** Find the **total resistance** in the circuit opposite.

**b)** What current will the ammeter show?

**c)** Calculate the **voltmeter reading** for Meter 1 and Meter 2.

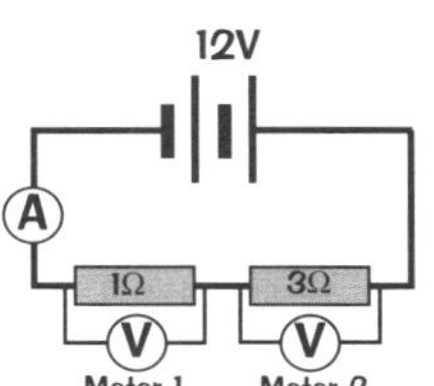


**Q9** **Complete the following**, *using these words:* ***decreases, dimmer, up, increased, smaller***

If lamps are connected in ***series*** the current goes through all the lamps in turn. The more lamps you add, the ____________ they get. The ammeter reading ____________ because the current is ____________. This means the resistance in the circuit has ____________. When we add more resistors to a series circuit, the total resistance goes ____________.

# Series Circuits

**Q10** Study the circuit on the right.

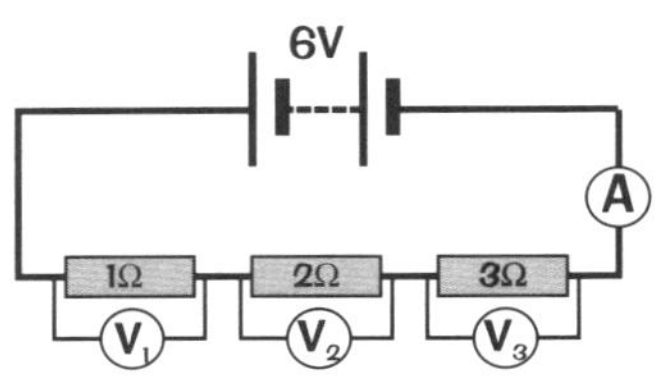


**a)** Calculate the total resistance in the circuit.

**b)** What current does the ammeter read?

**c)** Work out the voltmeter reading for meters 1, 2 and 3.

**Q11** *Look at the circuit opposite.*

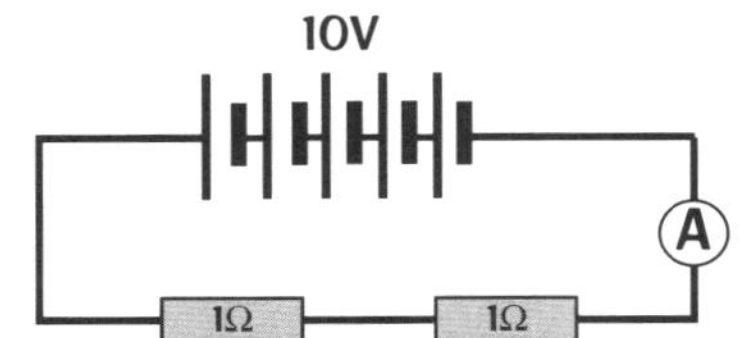


**a)** Find the **total** resistance.

**b)** The ammeter reading is 5A. If you wanted to reduce the current to 2A (using the same power supply and ammeter), how many **extra** 1Ω resistors would you have to connect in series?

**Q12** **Draw a circuit diagram** of a power supply, an ammeter and two resistors in series. *Voltmeters are connected in parallel with these resistors.* If the voltmeters read 4V and 20V and the current is 0.5A:

**a)** find the resistance of each resistor.

**b)** find the voltage supplied by the power supply.

**Q13** Look at the circuit opposite.

**Calculate** what each voltmeter, $V_1$, $V_2$, $V_3$ and $V_4$ will read.

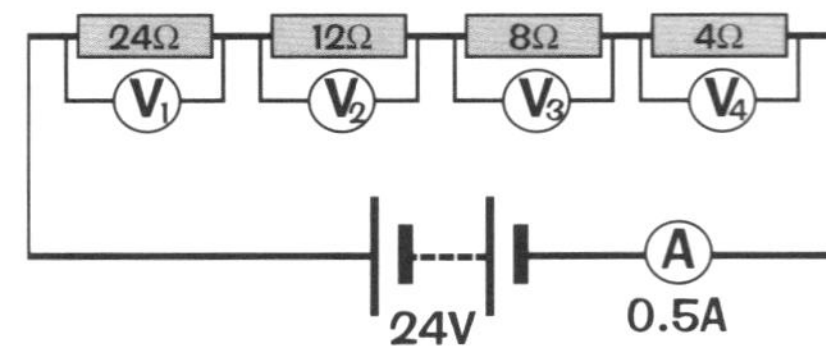


**Q14** Match the "Heads and Tails" to complete the statements about series circuits:

| Heads | Tails |
|---|---|
| **a)** The bigger the resistance of a component | the source voltage (power supply/cell/battery) |
| **b)** The size of the current is determined by | the sum of all the resistances |
| **c)** The same current is | the bigger its share of the total p.d. |
| **d)** The voltage in a series circuit always adds up to | in all parts of a series circuit |
| **e)** The total resistance is | the total p.d. of the cells and the total resistance of the circuit |

**Q15** **Complete the missing values** in this circuit diagram.

What is the potential difference across the 1.5Ω resistor and the 2.5Ω resistor (i.e., across X and Y)?

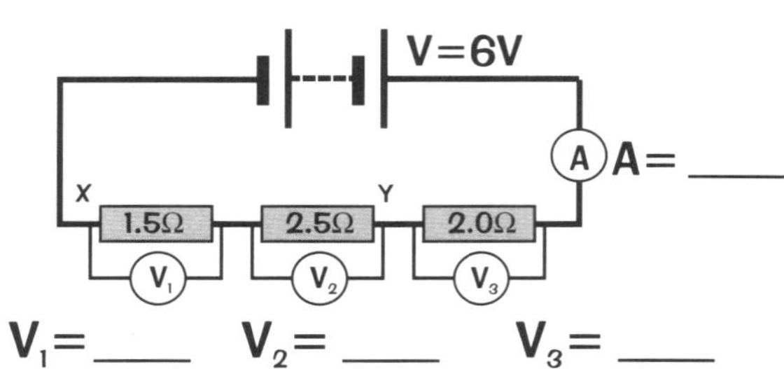


## Top Tips

Series circuits are really quite simple to understand. The components are connected one after the other between the +ve and –ve of the power supply (except the voltmeters, which are always connected in parallel). Also, everything in the circuit has the same current in it.

# Parallel Circuits

**Q1** **Draw** two lamps connected in parallel with a 6V battery and...

**a)** a switch to switch both lamps off at once.

**b)** a switch for each lamp.

**Q2** **Draw** a lamp connected in parallel with an electric motor. Both the lamp and the motor have their own switch. The power supply is 24V.

**Q3** The circuit below shows two lamps connected in parallel. Initially these lamps are of **normal brightness**. Work out the brightness of the lamp(s) when the following modifications **a)** to **d)** are carried out. Choose from **off**; **dimmer**; **normal**; **brighter**.

**a)** One lamp is unscrewed.

**b)** Another cell is added.

**c)** The cells are arranged in parallel.

**d)** Another bulb is added in parallel with the first bulbs.

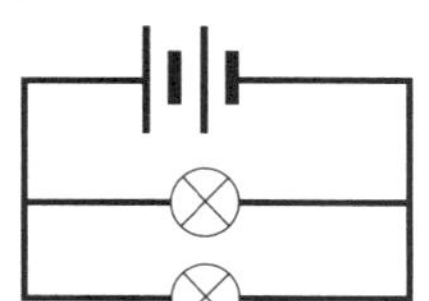

**Q4** *Everything electrical in a car is connected up in parallel.*
**Draw** a circuit diagram of a 12V power supply with a fan (motor), light and wiper (motor). Each device needs a separate switch.

**Q5** Study the circuits **a)** to **f)** below. There are only three different designs. Sort them into pairs of similar circuits.

**a)**
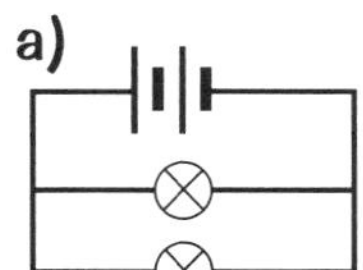
**b)**
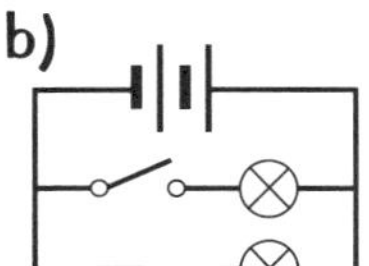
**c)**
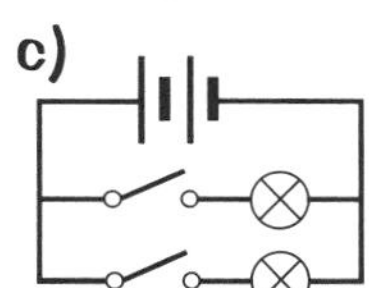
**d)**
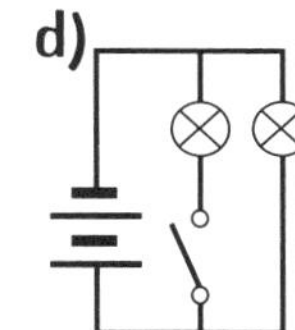
**e)**
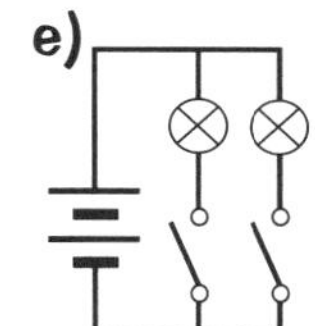
**f)**
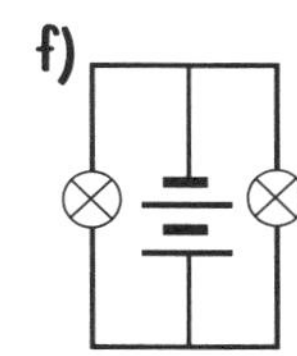

**Q6** Study the circuit diagram opposite. Which lamp(s) (1 → 5) are operated by switches A, B and C?

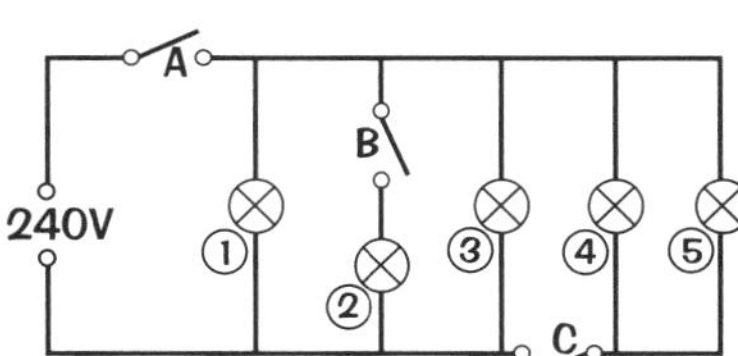


*Taking all switches to be closed to start with.*

Switch A operates: _________

Switch B operates: _________

Switch C operates: _________

**Q7** **Draw** a circuit with a 2Ω and a 4Ω resistor in parallel, running off a 6V battery.

**a)** What is the current in the 2Ω resistor?

**b)** What is the current in the 4Ω resistor?

**c)** What is the current in the cell?

**d)** *These two resistors are replaced with a single resistor, connected* **in series** *with the cell.* What would this resistance be if the current in the cell stayed the same?

**Q8** *The resistances of the resistors in the circuit opposite are identical. The ammeter reads 1A.* What is the resistance of these resistors?

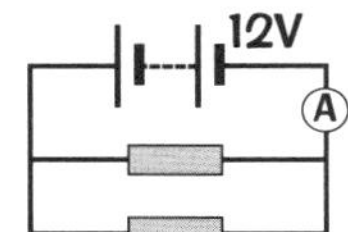


**Q9** Draw a circuit diagram of a 12V power supply and two resistors, 6Ω and 3Ω, connected in parallel. Find the current in each resistor and in the power supply. Mark the currents on your circuit diagram.

**Q10** Draw these three resistors in parallel with a 24V power supply. 4Ω 3Ω 2Ω
Write on the diagram the current in the cell and the current in each of the resistors.

# Parallel Circuits

Q11 Match the statements a) → e) about parallel circuits:

Heads

Tails

| Heads | Tails |
|---|---|
| a) The voltage is the same | across each branch in parallel. |
| b) The total current is | less than the smallest resistance of any branch. |
| c) The current in each component | depends on its resistance. |
| d) The total resistance is | the bigger the current. |
| e) The lower the resistance | equal to the sum of all currents in separate branches. |

Q12 a) Look at the diagram opposite and complete the following:
Use these words: less, branch, parallel, $A_2$ and $A_3$, more, $A_1$

**If lamps are connected in ______________, the current in the main part of the circuit splits up and goes through each ______________. The brightness of the lamps stays the same the ________ lamps you add in ______________. The ammeter reading at ______________ is lower than at (A) but is the same as those at ______________. The total resistance of lamps in parallel is ______________ than the resistance of any of the individual lamps.**

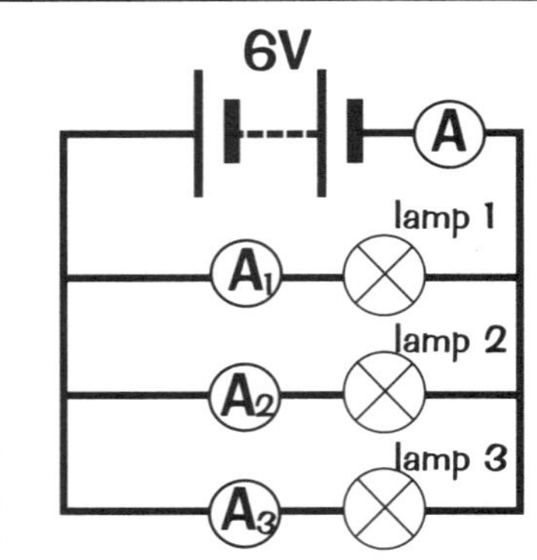


b) Look at the diagram again. Work out the total resistance of the lamps if each lamp has a resistance of 3Ω. Find the current in A, $A_1$, $A_2$ and $A_3$.

Q13 Look at the two circuits opposite.

a) Find the current in each of the parallel branches of circuit (b)

b) Find the current in the main branch of both circuits.

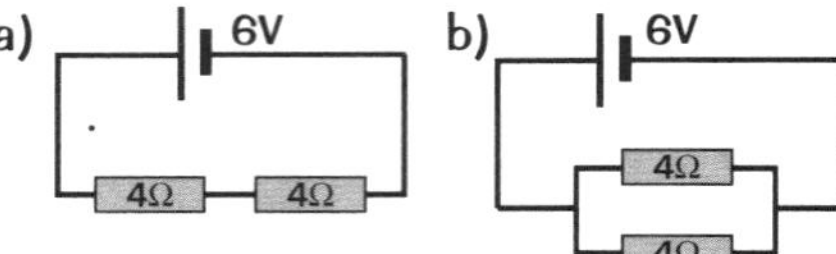


Q14 Find the current in the circuit (left) when:

a) switch A only is closed.

b) switch B only is closed.

c) Find the current through the 2 branches (through the 1Ω resistor and the 3Ω resistor). Then find the current in the circuit when both switches are closed.

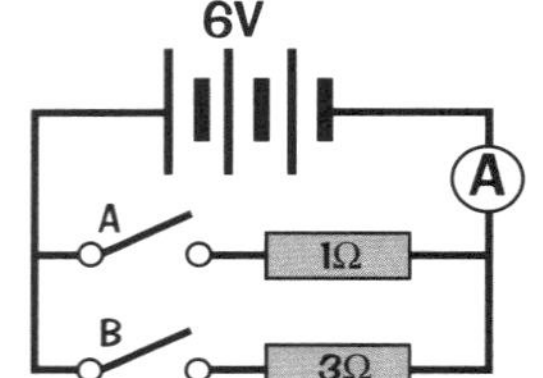


Q15 Study the circuit diagram below and complete the table.

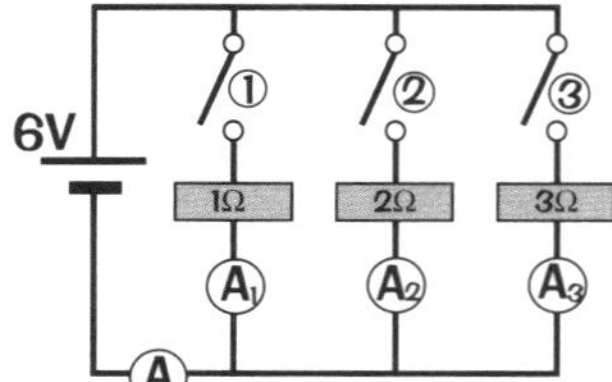


| Switch closed | Reading of current on ammeter | | | |
|---|---|---|---|---|
| | A | $A_1$ | $A_2$ | $A_3$ |
| 1 and 2 | | | | |
| 1 and 3 | | | | |
| 1, 2, and 3 | | | | |

## Top Tips

Parallel circuits are more sensible than series circuits — you can switch everything on and off separately. Remember that the voltage across each component is the same as the source voltage, and the current depends on its resistance. The total resistance is always less than the smallest resistance in the circuit.

# Static Electricity

**Q1** Complete the sentences below:

| | |
|---|---|
| **a)** Positive (+) and negative (–) charges | — is caused by friction. |
| **b)** Static electricity | — repel each other. |
| **c)** Negative charges (–) | — by connecting it to Earth. |
| **d)** Voltage | — the greater the voltage. |
| **e)** Induced charge | — repel each other. |
| **f)** The greater the charge | — are attracted to each other. |
| **g)** Discharge a conductor | — builds up if charge builds up. |
| **h)** Two negative (–) charges | — is lost if the charged rod is moved away. |
| **i)** Electrons | — move, never the positive charges. |
| **j)** Two positive (+) charges | — are left on a rod if electrons are rubbed off. |
| **k)** Positive charges (+) | — are found on a rod if electrons are rubbed on. |

**Q2** *The diagram opposite shows a duster and a polythene rod.*
Copy the diagram and use arrows to show the movement of charge when the rod is rubbed with a duster, and the charge left on each object.

Polythene rod

**Q3** **Arrange** the following statements in the correct order to explain how static is transferred to an acetate rod when it is rubbed by a cloth duster.

...the rod to the cloth.

...and the rod becomes

...positively charged.

...electrons are transferred from...

...negatively charged

So the cloth becomes...

If you rub an acetate rod with a cloth...

**Q4** These two rods, [+++++++] [– – – – – – –] attract each other with a force $F_0$. Study the pairs of rods below and write down if they attract with a force more than or less than $F_0$. Explain your answers.

a) [+++++++] [– – – – – – –]

b) [+++++++] [vertical – – – – – – – rod]

c) [+++++++] [– – – – – – –] (further apart)

d) [+ + + + + +] [– – – – – –]

**Q5** **a)** Copy the writing about the rod opposite, and **fill in the blanks**:

Use these words: ***charge, negative, equal, like charges repel, no, positive***

+ – + – + – + – + –
– + – + – + – + – +

> **This rod carries ___________ overall charge. It has ___________ numbers of ___________ and ___________ charges. The + and – signs represent the distribution of positive and negative ___________. Instead of forming areas of positive charge and areas of negative charge they spread out because___________________________**

A positively charged object is held near to this copper rod.

**b)** **Draw** the new arrangement of positive (+) and negative (–) charges in the metal rod. **Explain** the pattern.

**c)** One end of the metal rod is attracted to the positively charged object and the other end is repelled. The force of attraction is greater than the force of repulsion.

**Explain why this is.**

copper rod

# Static Electricity

**Q6** *Static electricity can be used to spray paint a car door.*

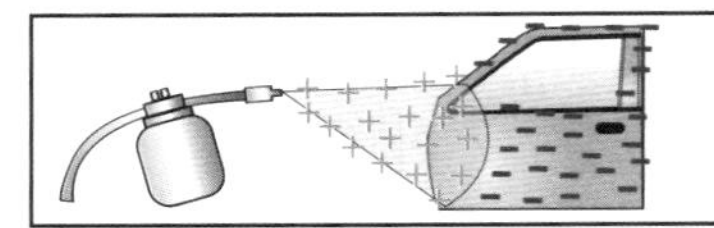

**Complete the following:**

Use these words:
***repel, spread out, positively, attracted, positive, earth, a negative terminal***

The spray paint nozzle is connected to a ________ terminal. This makes the spray drops __________ charged. This makes them ________ each other and so they ________ _____. The door is connected to the ________ or ________ so that the droplets are __________ to it.

**Q7** **Draw a simple diagram** to show how static electricity is made use of in a photocopier to position the black toner where it is needed.

**Q8** **a)** Explain how a moving car can become positively charged.

**b)** What do you feel if you touch the door of a charged car? Explain why this happens.

**Q9** Why do you sometimes get a shock from your jumper when you take it off? Use the following terms in your answer: "static charges", "movement of electrons", "sparks/shocks".

**Q10** **Draw a diagram** to show how lightning occurs. Include on your diagram: the cloud, raindrops, Earth, and positive and negative charges.

**Q11** *Static electricity can be lethal...*

**a)** **List** 3 working situations where static can lead to dangerous sparks in the workplace.

**b)** Choose one situation you listed in **a)** Draw a diagram to show how the static builds up. **Label** the (+) and (–) charges.

**c)** For your example in (**b**) , **explain** carefully the solution to the problem.

**Q12** Lightning conductors...

**a)** Why do tall buildings have lightning conductors?

**b)** What are lightning conductors made of?

**c)** Explain how a lightning conductor works.

**Q13** **Describe** how you could make 2 pieces of clingfilm:

**a)** attract each other.
**b)** repel each other.

## Top Tips

Static electricity — it's all about charges that aren't free to move, but discharge with a spark when they do finally move. Build up of static is caused by **friction**. Don't forget that **only electrons move**; if they are rubbed **on**, an object gets a **negative** charge; if they are rubbed **off**, an object gets a positive charge.

# Energy in Circuits

**Q1** Use these words to **fill in** the following paragraph about this circuit:

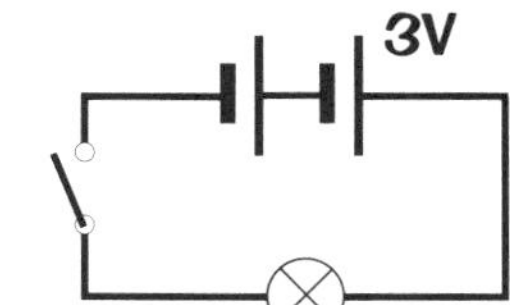


*energy, light, heat, electrical, transferred, cells, charge, two, light, voltage, flow, brighter, electric circuit, broken*

When the switch is closed, __________ flows around the circuit and the lamp lights up. The 3V battery is made up of ______ 1.5V ________. The energy is __________ by the __________ __________ to the lamp. The lamp converts _________ energy to _________ and ________ energy; the _______ energy being the useful output. If the switch is open, the circuit is __________ and there is no charge _________ and no transfer of __________. When the battery ___________ is increased to 6V, the lamp glows ______________ and more electrical energy is transferred than with the 3V battery.

**Q2** *Electrical energy can be converted to other useful forms of energy.*

In the 4 examples opposite, **name** the form(s) that electrical energy is transferred into.

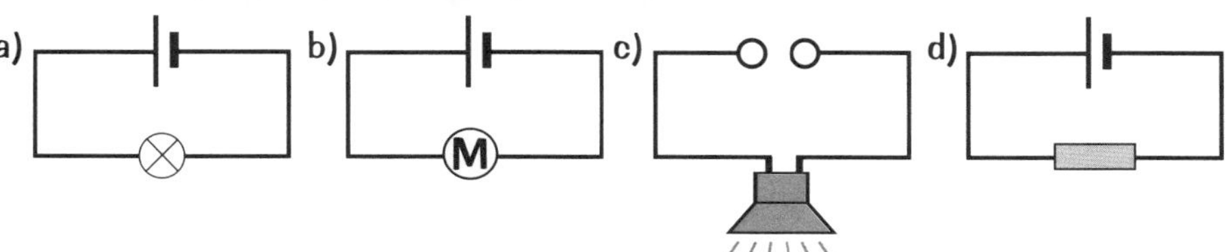


**Q3** Look at the diagram opposite which shows a water heating experiment. The experiment is run for a certain time and the water temperature is measured. How will the temperature compare if we:

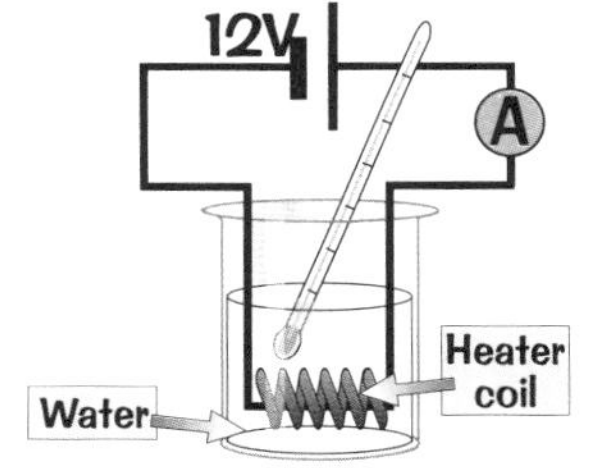


**a)** increase the voltage to 24V?
**b)** replace the heating coil with one of half the resistance?
**c)** replace the coil with a shorter one of the same total resistance?

**Q4** Data taken from a heating experiment is shown in the table opposite.

| Temperature (°C) | Time (minutes) |
|---|---|
| 20 | 0 |
| 40 | 1 |
| 58 | 2 |
| 71 | 3 |
| 82 | 4 |
| 87 | 5 |
| 94 | 6 |
| 100 | 7 |
| 100 | 8 |

**a)** Plot the graph of temperature (°**C**) against time (min).
**b)** **Explain** the shape of the curve. Why does the temperature stop rising after 7 minutes.
**c)** What was the temperature of the water after 2½ minutes and 5½ minutes?
**d)** If a wire of higher resistance replaces the wire in the heater coil, will it take more time or less time to boil the water? **Explain** your answer.
**e)** What **safety precautions** might you take during this experiment?
**f)** **How** could you make your readings **more** accurate?

**Q5** Answer the following questions.

**a)** **What happens** to some of the electrical energy when there is a current in a resistor?
**b)** What is the effect of increasing the **current** on the amount of heat energy produced?
**c)** What is the effect of increasing the **voltage** on the amount of heat energy produced?
**d)** What is the effect of increasing the circuit's **resistance** on the amount of heat energy produced?
**e)** What measuring instrument would you use to find the quantity of heat produced?

# Energy in Circuits

**Q6** Match the quantities **a)** → **e)** with their correct description on the right:

| | | |
|---|---|---|
| **a)** One volt | — | is the energy transferred per unit of charge passed. |
| **b)** Energy | — | is current x time. |
| **c)** One ampere | — | is one coulomb every second. |
| **d)** Voltage | — | is one joule per coulomb. |
| **e)** Charge | — | is charge x voltage. |

**Q7** Complete the two tables below.

| What it is? | Letter | Unit | Symbol |
|---|---|---|---|
| Voltage | V | volts | V |
| Current | I | | |
| | | ohms | Ω |
| | E | joules | |
| Electrical Charge | Q | | |
| | t | seconds | |
| Power | | watts | |

| If a current of: | flows for: | -then the charge passing is |
|---|---|---|
| 1 ampere | 1 second | 1 coulomb |
| 2 amperes | 1 second | |
| 2 amperes | 2 seconds | |
| 4 amperes | 3 seconds | |
| 5 amperes | | 15 coulombs |
| 6 amperes | 5 seconds | |
| 10 amperes | 6 seconds | |

**Q8** Find the energy supplied by a torch battery, voltage 6V, if 1500C of charge flows.

**Q9** Find the missing values of energy, charges and voltage in the table below.

| Energy (J) | Charge (C) | Voltage (V) |
|---|---|---|
| 500 | 50 | |
| | 15 | 3 |
| 4800 | | 240 |
| 10 000 | | 20 |
| | 75 | 12 |

**Q10** Join up these "cuttings". Begin with: "If a voltage in a circuit is changed from..."

and if the current is 3A the battery will supply 36 J/s to the circuit.

6V to 12V

is 36W.

by changing the battery,

4Ω.

The total resistance of the circuit must therefore be

each electric charge passing through the battery

will pick up twice the amount of energy.

So each coulomb of charge will now carry

12J of energy,

So the power supplied

## Top Tips

This is all just another way of looking at electrical circuits. You can think of voltage pushing the charge round (creating a current), and resistance opposing the flow — or you can think of each component converting electrical energy into other forms of energy, which is marginally more exciting.

# The Cost of Domestic Electricity

**Q1** Look at these two electricity bills from Rippov Electricity:

a) Complete the missing figures in these bills.

b) What is the scientific name for the term "units"?

c) If you were estimating the meter reading for a further quarter, what might it be?

| | | | |
|---|---|---|---|
| Previous meter reading: | 47041 | Previous meter reading: | 26935 |
| Present meter reading: | 47525 | Present meter reading: | 27601 |
| Number of units used: | ........ | Number of units used: | ........ |
| Cost per unit (pence): | 7.35 | Cost per unit (pence): | 7.35 |
| Cost of electricity used: | ........ | Cost of electricity used: | ........ |
| Fixed quarterly charge: | £9.49 | Fixed quarterly charge: | £9.49 |
| Total bill: | ........ | Total bill: | ........ |
| VAT on Total bill at 8.0%: | ........ | VAT on Total bill at 8.0%: | ........ |
| Final total: | £48.67 | Final total: | £63.12 |

d) If the bills were for the Summer quarter (May, June and July) what **difference** might you expect in a bill for the Winter quarter (November, December and January)? Explain your answer.

**Q2** *Here are some electrical appliances used at home:*

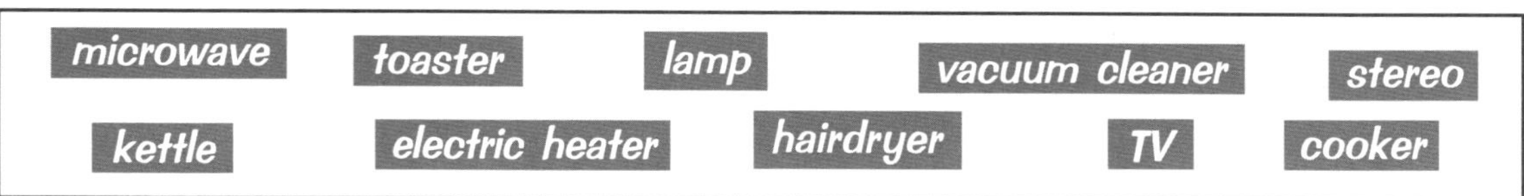


Which four appliances are the most expensive to run (for a given length of time)? What do they have in common?

**Q3** Fill in the gaps below.

| | |
|---|---|
| a) These are units of energy: ____________ <br> b) These are units of power: ____________ <br> "Units": kWh, J, kJ, kW, W | c) "deci" means: ____________ <br> d) "kilo" means: ____________ <br> 10, 100, 1000, 10,000, $\frac{1}{10}$, 100,000 |

**Q4** Fill in the table opposite to help you work out how many joules a hairdryer uses in one hour...

| | |
|---|---|
| Power (kilowatts): | 1 kW |
| Time switched on (in hours): | 1 h |
| Power in watts: | ........ |
| Time switched on (seconds): | ........ |
| Energy used (in kilowatt hours): | ........ |
| Energy used (in joules): | ........ |

**Q5** Complete this table. The first one is done for you.

| Appliance | Rating(kW) | Time(h) | Energy (kWh) | Cost at 10p per unit |
|---|---|---|---|---|
| Storage Heaters | 2 | 4 | $2 \times 4 = 8$ | $8 \times 10 = 80$p |
| Cooker | 7 | 2 | | |
| 1-bar Electric Fire | 1 | 1.5 | | |
| Kettle | 2 | 0.1 | | |
| Iron | 1 | 1.2 | | |
| Refrigerator | 0.12 | 24.0 | | |
| Lamp | 0.06 | 6.0 | | |
| Radio Cassette | 0.012 | 2.0 | | |

[Cost of electricity = power (kW) x time (h) x cost of 1kWh.]

# The Cost of Domestic Electricity

**Q6** Complete the following summary using words from this list:

*joules energy energy twice voltage previous take*

To find the number of units used on an electricity bill, ____________ the ____________ from the present meter reading. You pay for the ____________ you have used, not the ____________ or current supplied. If a label on an appliance says "1kW" it means it will use ____________ at the rate of 1000 ____________ per second. A "2kW" appliance uses energy ____________ as quickly as a "1kW" appliance.

**Q7** Calculate the energy consumed by the following (in kWh):

**a)** 100W lamp for 10 hours
**b)** 10W mains radio for 5 hours
**c)** 500W microwave for 1/2 hour
**d)** 100W electric blanket for 1 hour

**Q8** Find the cost (at 10p/unit) of using:

**a)** An electric drill, power 300W for 2 hours.
**b)** A 20W hairstyling brush for 1/2 hour.
**c)** Two 100W electric lights on for 9 hours a day for a week.
**d)** A 900W toaster for 15 minutes every day for a month (30 days — it's September!).
**e)** Four 60W electric lights on 12 hours a day for an old-fashioned working week (5 days).

**Q9** *The picture shows a manual for a 60W stereo radio that runs off the mains.*

**a)** Calculate how long the radio takes to consume 1kWh.
**b)** What assumption are you using in your answer to part **a)**?

**Q10** In the following questions, work out which of the two appliances consumes the most energy.

**a)** A 2kW heater for 4 hours *or* a 3kW fire for 3 hours.
**b)** A 900W toaster for 15 minutes *or* a 800W vacuum cleaner for 20 minutes.
**c)** A 300W drill for $^1/_2$ hour *or* a 100W light bulb for 1 $^1/_2$ hours.
**d)** A 1kW iron for 1 hour *or* a 2kW kettle for 20 minutes.
**e)** A 2.1kW immersion heater for 1 hour *or* a 1.5kW fire for $^1/_2$ hour.

**Q11** *The following table summarises the initial and running costs of filament lamps and CFL (compact fluorescent) lamps.*

| Type of Lamp | Lifetime of lamp (h) | Power (kW) | Cost of 1kWh of electricity (£) | Cost of electricity for lamp's lifetime (£) | Cost of 1 lamp (£) | Total running and purchase cost for 12000 hr. (£) |
|---|---|---|---|---|---|---|
| CFL | 12000 | 0.02 | 0.1 | | 10.00 | |
| Filament | 1000 | 0.1 | 0.1 | | 0.50 | |

**a)** Copy and complete the table.
**b)** Give two benefits of CFL lamps over filament lamps. *(A 20W CFL lamp gives the same amount of light as a 100W filament lamp.)*

## Top Tips

The units that electricity meters measure are kilowatt-hours (kWh), and that means the amount of electrical energy used by a 1kW appliance left on for 1 hour. Don't be confused by the name, it isn't a measurement of power.

# Plugs and Fuses

**Q1** State the electrical hazard in each diagram below, and say what you would do to make each one safe:

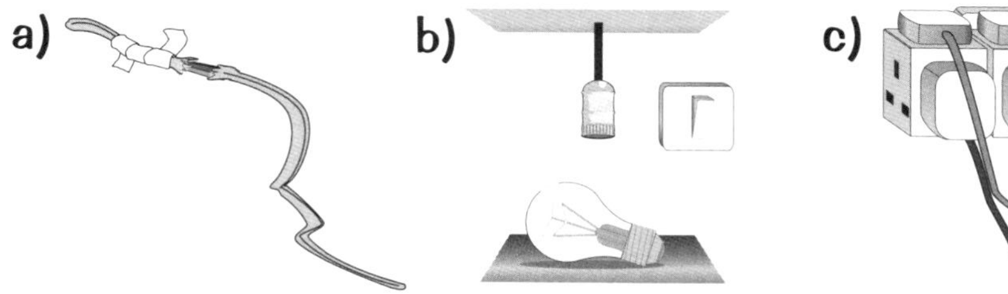


**Q2** Write down as many other electrical hazards in the home that you can think of. You should be able to write down at least six others.

**Q3** *These are the hazard signs on a hairdryer leaflet.*

Explain what they mean and why they need to be marked on the hairdryer.

**Q4** *Plugging into the mains:*

Label the plug on the right with: green and yellow; blue; brown; live; earth; neutral.

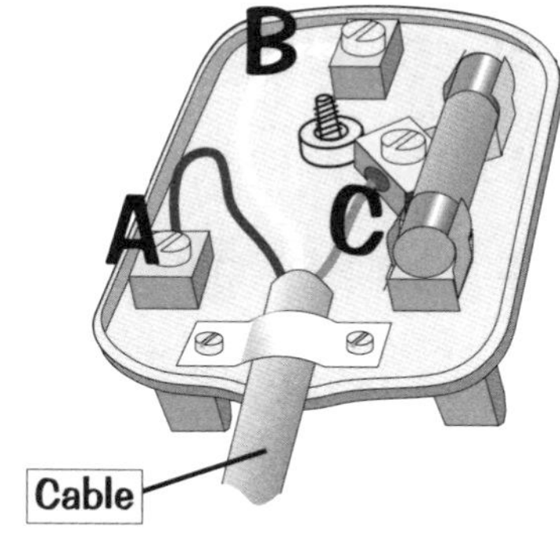


**Q5** Which parts of the plug are made out of the following materials, and why?

**a)** brass or copper

**b)** plastic

**Q6** Write a check list of five things you would check to make sure a newly wired plug is completely safe.

**Q7** *Radios, TVs and lamps do not usually have an earth wire.*

**a)** What is the function of the earth wire?

**b)** Why are appliances like TVs safe to use without an earth wire?

**Q8** Complete the following paragraph:

Use these words: safety, alternating, neutral, live, 230, earth, voltage

> The ____________ of a live wire is an ____________ voltage of ________V.
> Electricity normally flows along the ____________ and ______________ wires only. The ______ wire is just for ______________.

**Q9** Find out about and describe the extra safety features used for electric lawnmowers, hedge trimmers and drills.

# Plugs and Fuses

**Q10** *The table opposite shows 7 appliances and the current in them.*

For each appliance, decide if it needs a 3A, 5A or a 13A fuse.

(the first one is done for you)

| Appliance | Current taken (A) | Fuse value (A) |
|---|---|---|
| Food Mixer | 2 | 3 |
| Cassette Player | 3 | |
| Hairdryer | 4 | |
| Electric Heater | 12 | |
| Toaster | 4 | |
| Kettle | 9 | |
| Vacuum Cleaner | 3.5 | |

**Q11** *Answer the following questions on fuses.*

**a)** Why do we use fuses?

**b)** What is **inside** a fuse?

**c)** **Explain** what happens when a fault causes a 6A current in an appliance fitted with a 3A fuse?

**d)** Why should you not use a 1A fuse in a hairdryer plug?

**e)** **Explain** what would happen if the live wire in a toaster touched the metal case. Say how the **earth wire** and the **fuse** work together to make the appliance safe.

**Q12** *This diagram shows a kettle circuit that has been drawn incorrectly.*

**a)** Find the 4 mistakes.

**b)** **Redraw** the circuit correctly.

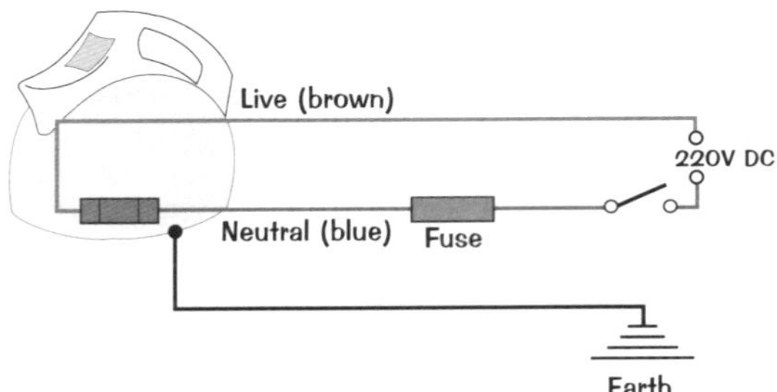


**Q13** **Fill in the gaps** in the box below, using the given words.

*cover  blown  expert  wired  fuse  earth  replace*

| | |
|---|---|
| Appliance: | Must be correctly __________ to a plug fitted with the correct __________ and with an __________ wire connected to any touchable metal part. |
| Blown Fuses: | You must find out why a fuse has __________. If this is not obvious, consult an __________. Do not __________ the fuse with one of a higher rating. |
| Fire Risk: | Never __________ an appliance, particularly with something that can burn. |

**Q14** Study the diagram opposite of a domestic electricity supply. What happens to the lights in the kitchen, lounge and dining room if:

**a)** fuse 1 blows?

**b)** fuse 2 blows?  **c)** fuse 3 blows?

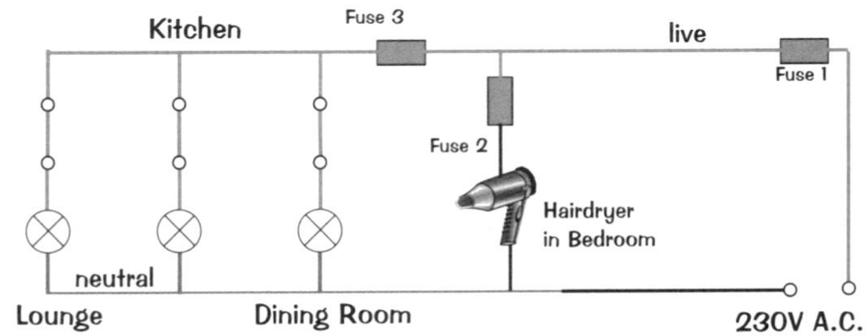


## Top Tips

Now, you already know that electricity is dangerous and it can kill you. What you have to do here is to be able to name all the possible **electrical hazards** in the home and say how to **eliminate** them. This is actually just common sense. Don't forget that you need to know how to wire a plug.

# The National Grid and Mains Electricity

**Q1** *The diagram below shows how electricity is made in power stations, and sent to homes and industry.*

a) **Complete** the **labels** on the diagram.

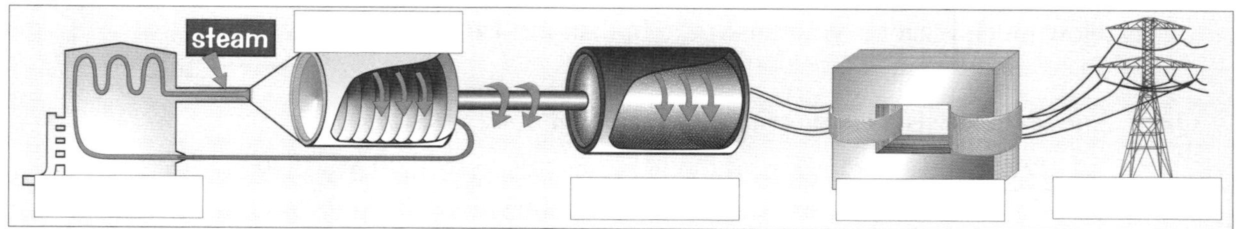


b) **Complete** the following using these words:

*induction, oil, uranium fuel, steam, gas, coal, turbine, generator, magnetic*

Heat energy in a power station is produced by burning fossil fuels such as ____________, ___________ or ____________ . _________________ is used in nuclear power stations. The boiler makes ___________ which drives a ___________ , which turns a _________ . The generator produces electricity using the principle of electromagnetic __________. This happens when a metal coil is rotated in a strong ___________ field .

**Q2** **Match** these pairs of statements about the National Grid and Mains Electricity.

a) Cables are high voltage
b) Power supplied
c) To transmit a lot of power
d) A high current means a loss of heat
e) Power loss due to resistance in the cables
f) It's cheaper to boost the voltage up to 400,000V
g) Boosting the voltage up to 400,000V
h) Transformers step-up voltage
i) Transformers step-down voltage to our homes
j) Voltage has to be AC on the National Grid

- due to resistance of the cables
- requires transformers as well as big pylons with huge insulators
- equals $I^2 \times R$
- for efficient transmission
- best calculated using $V \times I$
- to keep the current low
- you need a high voltage or a high current
- and keep the current very low
- to bring it back to safe, useable levels
- because transformers don't work on D.C..

**Q3** *Letter Check! Are you getting confused by all these letters?* **Write down** what each one stands for.

a) Symbols for quantities: **i)** V **ii)** I **iii)** P **iv)** R

b) Letters for units: **i)** Ω **ii)** A **iii)** W **iv)** V

**Q4** Pair up the units in question 3 with the quantities they represent.

**Q5** **Pair up** the words..  ..and meanings below:

**a)** Transmit
**b)** AC
**c)** DC
**d)** Turbine
**e)** Power station
**f)** Transformer

- rotary motor driven by steam
- place for generating and distributing electrical power
- direct current
- send from one place to another
- changes the voltage of an alternating current supply
- alternating current

**Q6** *Mains voltage is 230V.* **Find the power of:**

a) a toaster which takes a current of 3A.

b) a drill which takes a current of 2A.

c) a television which takes a current of 0.5A.

# The National Grid and Mains Electricity

**Q7** *There is a current in a 5Ω resistor.*
Find the power if the current is: **a)** 2A **b)** 4A.
**c)** How much bigger is your answer to **b)** than **a)**? Explain why.

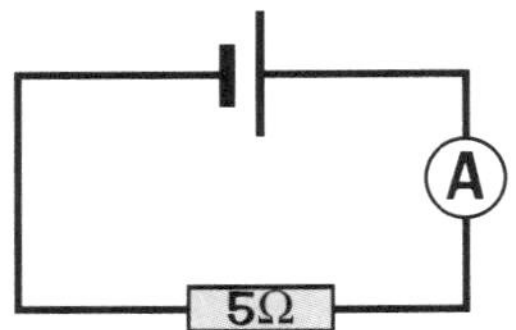


**Q8** Shown below is a circuit with 12V battery and 4Ω resistor.

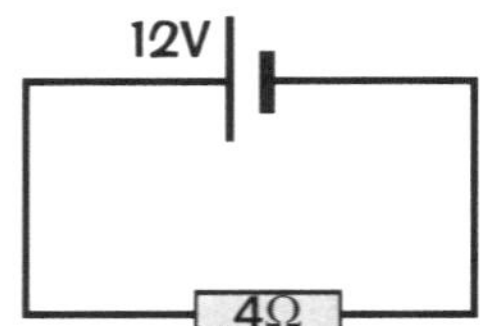


**a)** Find the power supplied by the battery to the resistor.
**b)** Find the power if the voltage is doubled to 24V.
**c)** Find the power if the resistor is replaced with one of 2W.

**Q9** Complete the table below. *(Take mains voltage as 230V)*

| Appliance | Power in kilowatts (kW) | Power in Watts (W) | Current in Amps (A) | Fuse: 3A or 13A? |
|---|---|---|---|---|
| Iron | 0.92 | | | |
| TV | 0.115 | | | |
| Kettle | 2.3 | | | |
| Video Recorder | 0.046 | | | |
| Fan Heater | 1.2 | | | |

**Q10** *A 1.5kW heater and a 2W clock work off a 230V mains electricity supply.* Work out:
**a)** The current taken by each.
**b)** The fuse needed in the plug of the heater and the clock. Why are they different?

**Q11** *The p.d. across 120, 3W fairy lights is 240V. The lights are in series.*
**a)** Find the voltage drop across each lamp. **b)** Find the current in each lamp.
**c)** Find the current in the whole circuit.

**Q12** *A cable can take a maximum current of 2A when supplied with a mains voltage of 230V.*
**a)** Find the maximum power that can be carried by the cable.
**b)** How many 60W bulbs in parallel can you run off the cable?

**Q13** Arrange these phrases into sentences:

A high current gives more power

to spend their energy every second.

because each electron carries more energy.

A high voltage gives more power

because there are more electrons

**Q14** What quantities do the following units represent: C/s, J/s, J/C?

## Top Tips

All power stations are more or less the same — they have a boiler that makes steam which turns a turbine which drives a generator, producing electricity.
Remember these formulae for power and when to use them: $P = VI$ $P = I^2R$ $P = V^2/R$.

# Magnetic Fields

**Q1** State whether these materials are magnetic or not;

| iron | copper | aluminium | brass | steel | silver | gold | nickel |
|---|---|---|---|---|---|---|---|

**Q2** *This question concerns sprinkling iron filings onto a piece of paper, with a magnet underneath.*

**a)** Where do most of the iron filings collect and why do they collect there?

**b)** Draw the pattern of the magnet field around a single bar magnet.
Put arrows on the field lines that point towards magnetic south.

**Q3** On the diagrams below, label the North and South poles of the magnets a, b, c and d.
State whether each pair of magnets are attracting or repelling each other.

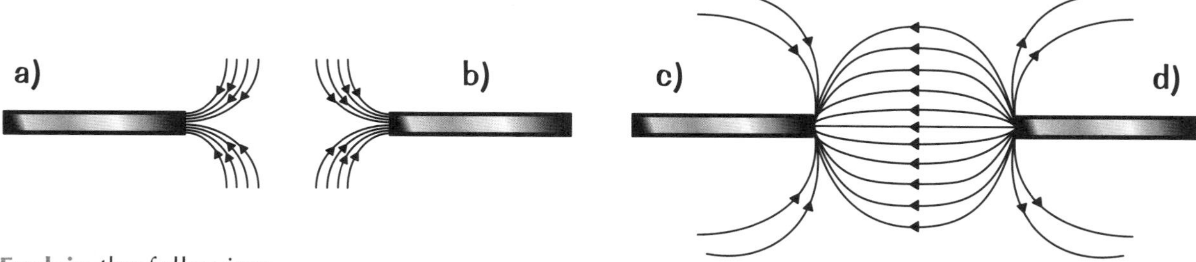


**Q4** Explain the following:

**a)** Magnets are often fitted to the doors of cupboards.

**b)** Flour is usually passed near a magnet before it is packed.

**c)** If a magnet is broken in half, each half is a magnet.

**d)** If an iron bar or a steel bar are near a magnet, they become magnetised.

**e)** If the bars in d) are taken away from the magnet, the steel bar keeps its magnetism, but the iron bar does not.

**Q5** *Suppose you were given a small bar magnet with nothing on it to tell you which was "S" and which was "N".*

**a)** Explain how you could find which end is "S" and which is "N" using another magnet with the poles correctly labelled.

**b)** Explain how you could do this without using another magnet with the poles already labelled "N" and "S".

**Q6** Use the following words to complete the sentences below (you will need to use one of the words more than once).

*suspended  south  opposite  poles  plotting  freely*

**Magnetic __________ are __________ to geographic poles: that is, the __________ magnetic pole is at the north pole. The black end of the black and white double arrow compass needle is the __________ pole. Any magnet __________ so that it can turn __________ will come to rest pointing north–south. A compass can also be used for __________ magnetic fields around bar magnets.**

**Q7** **a)** What navigational problem might mountaineers have if they come across magnetic rocks?

**b)** In what direction does a freely hanging magnet point at the magnetic North Pole?

**c)** In what direction does a compass needle point at the magnetic North Pole?

**d)** Towards which country would a compass needle point at the geographic North Pole?

# Magnetic Fields

**Q8** Put these phrases together to make a sentence describing magnetic fields.

| like iron and steel | is a region where | and also wires carrying currents |
|---|---|---|
| A magnetic field | magnetic materials | experience a force |
| | acting on them | |

**Q9** *This question is about the magnetic field around a current-carrying wire:*

**a)** *Compasses are put on card around a wire through which a high current flows up through it.* **Draw in** the direction the compass needles are pointing in figure **a)**.

a)

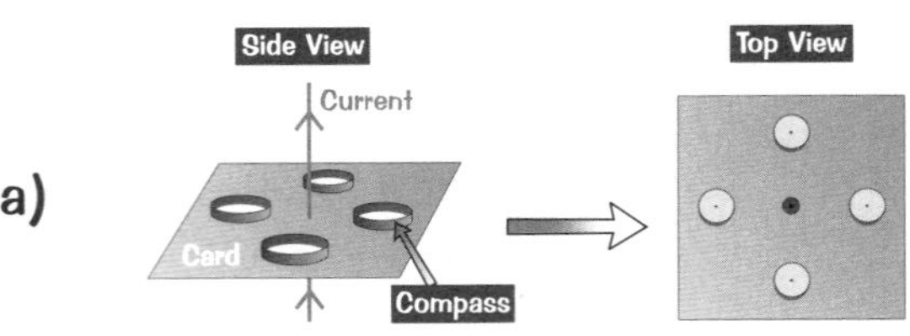


**b)** *The experiment was repeated with the current flowing DOWN through the card.* **Draw in** the direction the compass needles are now pointing in figure **b)**.

b)

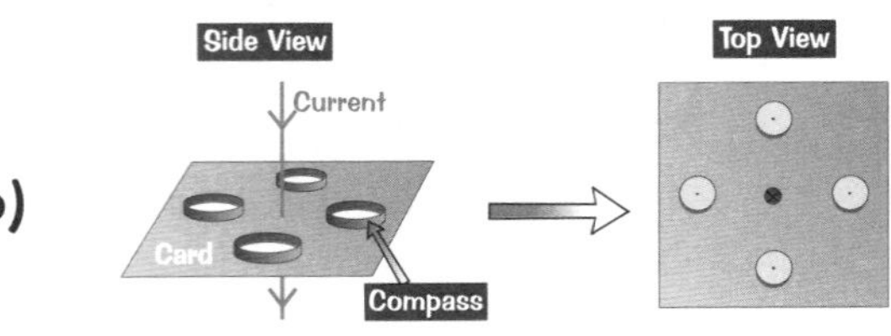


**c)** **Describe** a simple rule to work out the direction of the magnetic field around a wire through which an electric current flows.

**d)** **Choose** the correct words:
The magnetic field is stronger **closer to / further from** the wire. **Increasing / Decreasing** the current makes the magnetic field stronger. The field lines run **around / along** the wire.

**Q10** A magnetic field is produced when there is a current in a solenoid.

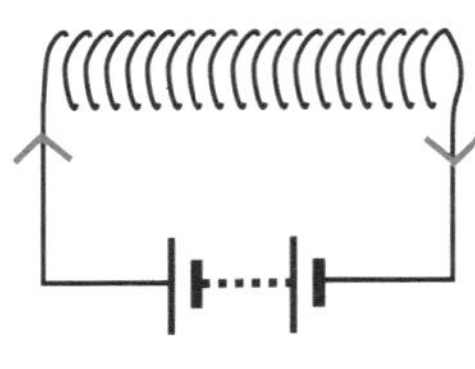

**a)** Copy the diagram opposite and draw in the magnetic field pattern surrounding the coil.

**b)** Describe the magnetic field **inside** the solenoid.

**c)** Describe two ways of **increasing** the strength of the magnetic field.

**Q11** *Four students set up different coils, all with the* **same current** *in the wires.*

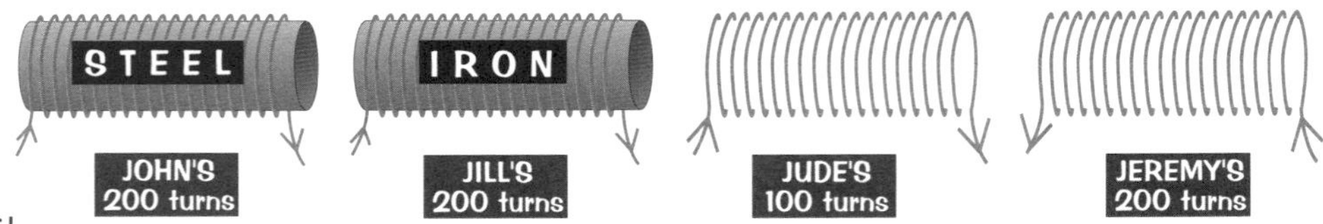


**a)** Whose coil:
- **i)** gives the **weakest** magnetic field?
- **ii)** has a South pole at the left-hand end?
- **iii)** will still possess a magnetic field when the current is **switched off**?

**b)** Is the wire in the coil insulated, and why?

## Top Tips

Learn this definition: A **magnetic field** is a region where **magnetic materials** (like iron and steel) and also **wires carrying currents** experience a **force** acting on them. The diagrams of a field around a magnet and a solenoid come up in the Exam, so learn the diagrams on questions 2,3 and 10a.

# Electromagnets and Electromagnetic Devices

**Q1** *Look at the diagram of this electromagnet.*

a) **Label** the diagram with these words:

iron core | solenoid | current in | current out | magnetic field pattern

b) **Explain** what an electromagnet is.

c) What is the purpose of the **iron core**?

d) Why is the core made of iron, and not say, copper?

e) Why is the core not made of steel?

f) Which end of the electromagnet is the north pole?

g) How could you make the north and south poles of the electromagnet swap around?

h) A plotting compass is placed at A, B, C, D and E. Draw which way the north end of the compass will point for each position.

i) Why does the wire around the core have to be insulated?

**Q2** *The strength of an electromagnet depends on three factors.*
**Unjumble** these words to reveal what these are...

| the | the | the | what | of | of | core | current | is |
|---|---|---|---|---|---|---|---|---|
| size | number | the | turns | of | of | the | coil | made |

**Q3** Look at the two solenoids below.

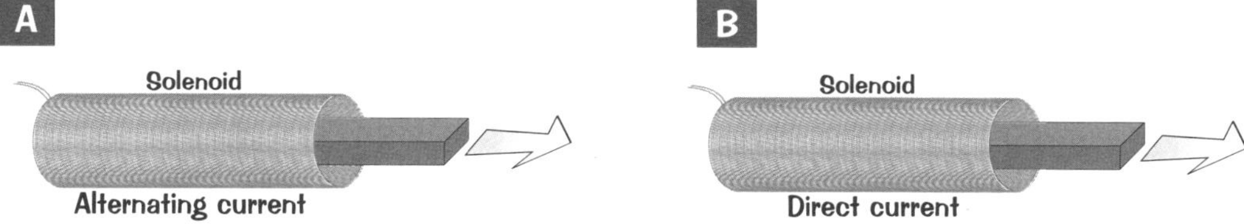


Decide if the solenoids in A and B are **magnetising** or **demagnetising** the steel bar. **Explain** the process in both cases.

**Q4** *An experiment was done to see how the number of paper clips an electromagnet can pick up varies with the current in it. The only trouble is, two of the readings are wrong. One was taken using a steel core instead of an iron one, and the other reading taken with a different solenoid with more coils.*

First of all, say why this is an example of **bad science**.

a) **Redraw the table** with the number of paperclips in order, and identify the 2 odd readings. (Label "more coils" and "steel core".)

b) **Plot a graph** of number of paperclips (vertical axis) against current, leaving out the two odd readings. **Draw** a "best fit" line.

c) **Make a labelled drawing** of the apparatus you would need to carry out this experiment.

| Number of paperclips | Current (A) |
|---|---|
| 13 | 3.0 |
| 4 | 1.0 |
| 8 | 2.0 |
| 3 | 1.5 |
| 1 | 0.5 |
| 2 | 1.0 |
| 14 | 3.5 |
| 5 | 1.5 |
| 11 | 2.5 |

# Electromagnets and Electromagnetic Devices

**Q5** a) Which circuits (x or y) match with the electromagnets in 'a' and 'b'.

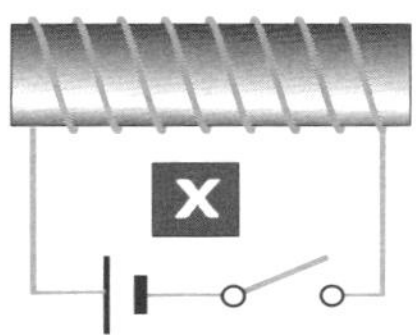


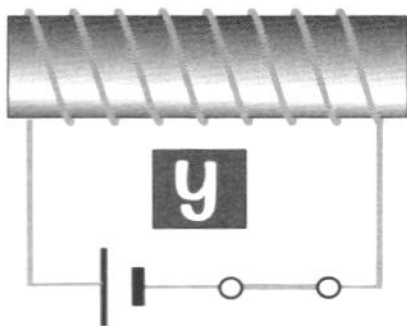

b) Explain briefly how the scrap yard electromagnet works. What are its main components?

**Q6** The diagram opposite shows a circuit breaker with the labels missing.

a) Label the diagram correctly using these words:

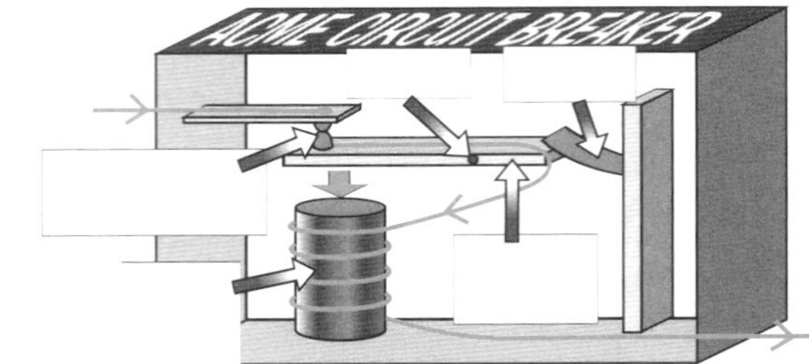


b) Put the following sentences about circuit breakers in order.

It can be reset manually. This trips the switch. The circuit breaker is placed on the incoming live wire. It will flick itself off again if the current is too high. If the current gets too high, the magnetic field in the coil pulls the iron rocker. This breaks the circuit.

**Q7** *The diagram opposite shows a starter motor relay.*

a) Draw in the missing right-hand part of the diagram, and label it.

b) What part of the car electrics uses a relay, and what is the relay's function?

c) Describe what happens in the relay when the switch is closed.

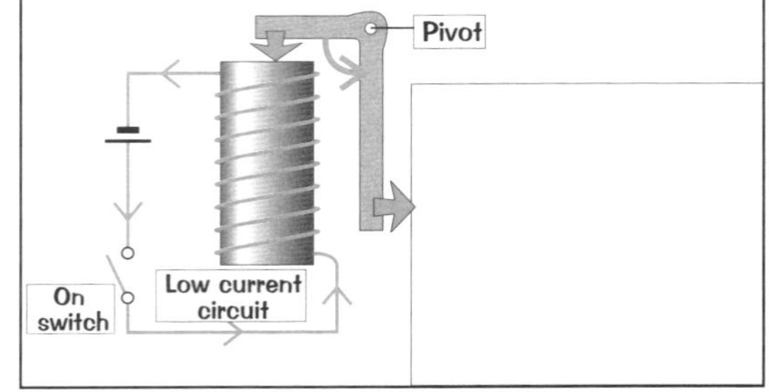


**Q8** *Someone closes the switch of this electric bell.*

a) What happens to the fixed iron cores?

b) Explain why the hammer moves and hits the gong.

c) *This movement breaks the circuit.* Explain why.

d) What happens to the iron bar after the hammer has hit the gong?

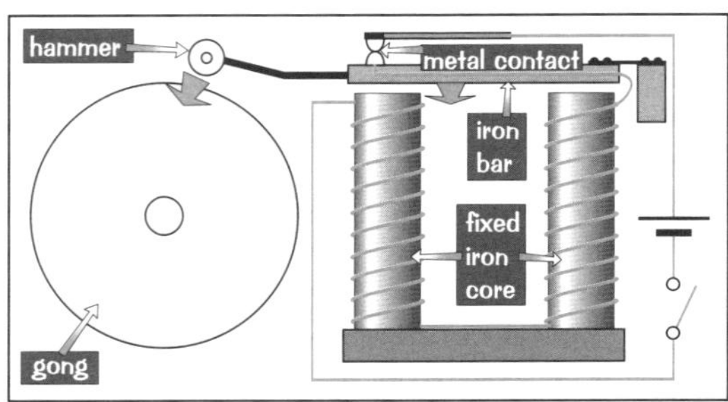


**Q9** Which of the following are magnetic materials?

iron copper zinc steel nickel brass

## Top Tips

Remember this essential definition: The strength of an electromagnet depends on three factors: the size of the current, the number of turns the coil has and what the core is made of. You also need to know the difference between iron and steel, and how to demagnetise a piece of steel.

# The Motor Effect

**Q1** The diagram opposite shows a current-carrying wire at right-angles to a magnetic field.

**a)** Use an arrow on the diagram to show the direction of the force experienced by the wire.

**b)** State two things you could do to increase the size of the force on the wire?

**c)** Describe the rule which predicts the direction of the force on the wire.

**d)** If the wire was turned through 90° so that it ran along the magnetic field, would there still be a force? Explain your answer.

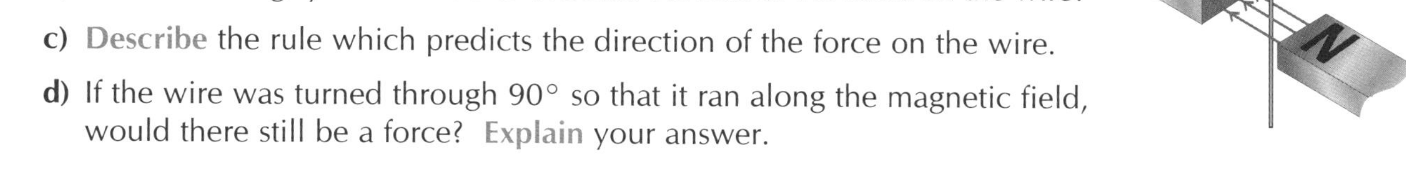


**Q2** The diagram opposite shows a horseshoe magnet. There is an electric current in a wire between the poles. A metal bar completes the circuit and rests freely on the wires.

Describe the motion of the bar when a direct current is switched on.

Describe the motion of the bar when an alternating current is switched on.

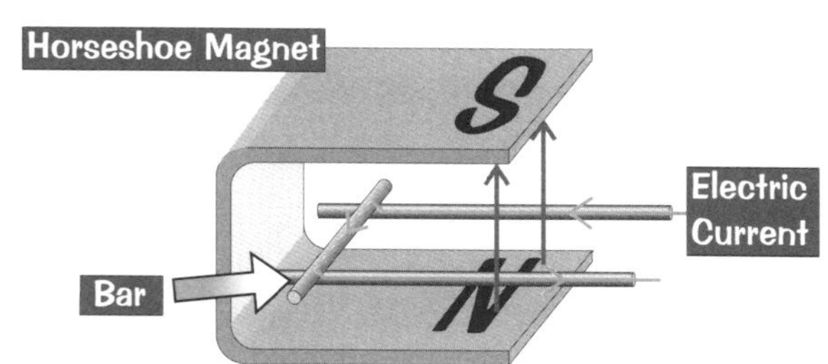


**Q3** Copy the diagram below showing two magnets with a current-carrying wire between them. Draw on the diagram:

**a)** The direction of the current.

**b)** The magnetic field and its direction (N to S).

**c)** The direction in which the wire will move.

**d)** State one way to make the wire move in the opposite direction.

**Q4** The diagram below shows a small laboratory version of a simple electric motor.

**a)** Name all the parts of the motor, labelled A to J.

**b)** Which of the parts from A to J are made from insulating materials?

**c)** There are three ways to increase the speed of the motor.

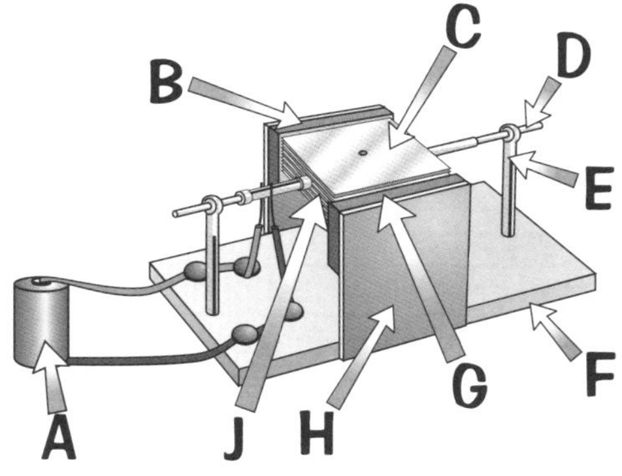


Fill in the gaps in the sentences opposite describing how to speed up the motor.

Use these words:

***turns, core, increase, iron***

1. Put more ______________ on the coil.
2. ______________ the magnetic field.
3. Put a ____________ ____________ in the coil.

# The Motor Effect

**Q5** *The diagram shows how a simple motor works. The coil is free to rotate between the poles of the magnet. The split ring commutator is fixed to the coil and turns with it.*

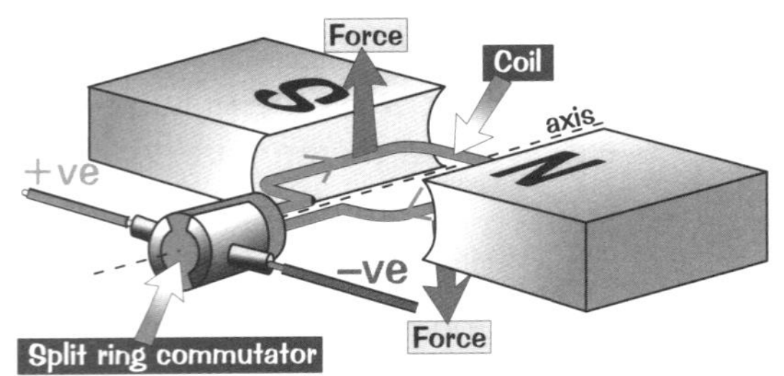


**Fill in the gaps** below using the **following words**:

*Current* *up* *torque* *coil* *forces* *turn* *down* *right*

When there is a current in the ___________ , the left side is pushed ___________ and the ___________ side ___________. When the coil is vertical, the forces can not ___________ it any further because there is no ___________. As the coil shoots past the vertical, the split ring commutator changes the direction of the___________. Now the ___________ point the other way around and the coil is pushed around and around and around...

**Q6** **Redraw** the circuit with an ammeter and a voltmeter correctly placed to measure the current in and voltage across the motor M.

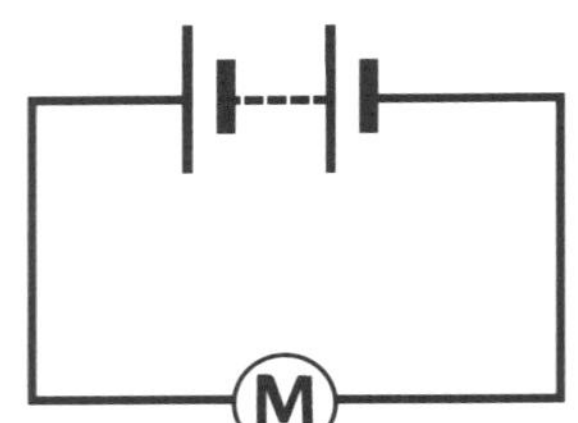


**Q7** **Name 5 appliances** at home that contain an electric motor.

**Q8** **Put these statements** about how a loudspeaker works into the **correct order**:

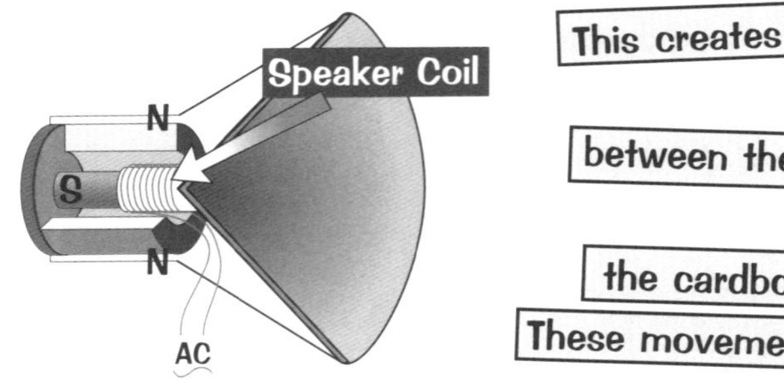


This creates sounds.

These make the coil move back and forth

between the poles of the magnet.

are fed into the speaker coil.

the cardboard case vibrate.

These movements make

AC signals from the amplifier

**Q9** **Link up** each description **a)** to **f)** with the correct word from the right-hand column.

|  |  |
|---|---|
| a) Swaps the contacts every half turn in an electric motor | • vibrates |
| b) Converts electrical energy into sound energy | • coil (armature) |
| c) Converts electrical energy into kinetic energy | • polarity |
| d) Turns around on an axis | • electric motor |
| e) Move quickly forwards and backwards but not changing position | • loudspeaker |
| f) Positive and negative | • split ring commutator |

## Top Tips

The best thing about the motor effect is looking at your left hand to answer the question (Believe me, in the Exam doing this will seem like entertainment). Remember thumb = motion, first finger = field and second finger = current. And it's Fleming's LEFT hand rule, important, so learn it.

# Electromagnetic Induction

**Q1** *A model train travels at high speed into a tunnel. A bar magnet is fixed to the top of the train. A coil of insulated wire is wound around the tunnel and underneath the track (connected in the circuit to a buzzer).*

a) **Explain why** the buzzer sounds when the train passes through the tunnel.

b) Would the buzzer sound if the train stopped in the tunnel? **Explain** your answer.

c) **Suggest two ways** to make the buzzer sound louder (without dismantling the tunnel).

**Q2** *A magnet is being pushed towards a coil of insulated wire.*

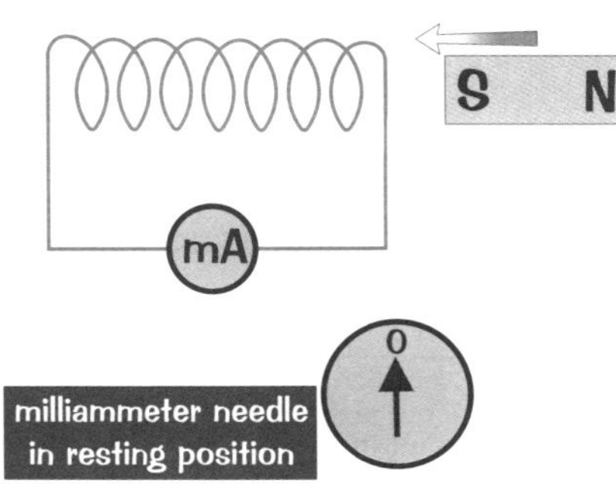


| Magnet pushed in | Needle moved to the right |
|---|---|
| Magnet in the coil - not moving | |
| Magnet pulled out | |
| Magnet pulled out faster | |

a) The table above summarises four experiments with the magnet. Copy and complete.

b) Which **type** of pole (N or S) is produced at the ends of the coil when the magnet is pushed in? **Explain** your answer.

c) Suggest **two** ways to reverse the poles produced in the coil.

**Q3** *A wire is moved upwards through a magnetic field, as shown in the diagram below.*

a) **What** is the direction of the induced current?
Is it: X to Y or Y to X?

b) What would be the effect of:

i) using a **stronger** magnet.

ii) moving the wire **faster**.

iii) moving the wire **downwards**.

iv) moving the wire towards one of the **poles**.

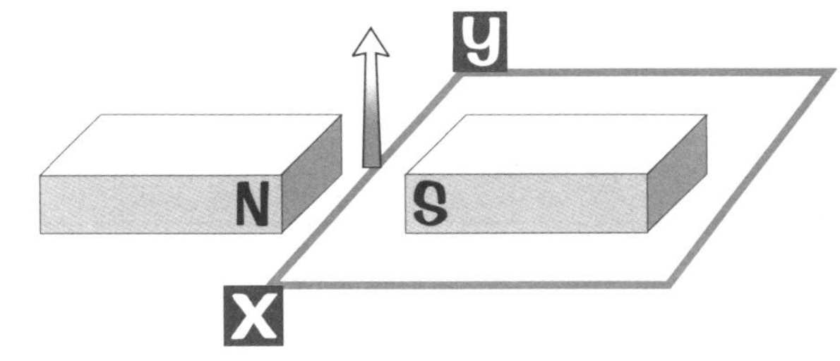


**Q4** The *size* of the induced voltage depends on...

a) **Unjumble** these words to reveal the **four factors**.

| *The the The the The The the the speed coil area turns strength of of of of on number magnet coil movement* |
|---|

b) Unjumble the following sentence about cutting magnetic flux lines.

*The size of the of cutting is proportional to the voltage induced rate of the field lines.*

# Electromagnetic Induction

**Q5** *Word check!* **Match** up the following words and phrases **a)** to **f)**:

| |
|---|
| a) North pole |
| b) South pole |
| c) Milliammeter |
| d) Coils |
| e) Dynamos |
| f) Alternating current |

| |
|---|
| • Measures small amounts of current |
| • Type of current produced by an alternator |
| • A generator needs more of these for more current |
| • Field lines point away from this pole |
| • When turned, they produce currents |
| • Field lines point towards this pole |

**Q6** **Fill in** the missing words about generators.

*Swap slip motor voltage rotate higher more voltage faster magnetic*

Generators __________ a coil in a __________ field. Their construction is quite like a __________, except there are __________ rings instead of a split ring commutator, so the contacts don't __________ every half turn. This means they produce alternating __________ as shown on the CRO displays. __________ revolutions produce not only __________ peaks, but __________ overall __________ too.

**Q7** *Below is a CRO display for a generator.* **Fill in the trace** to show how the current from a generator changes as the coil rotates, and also the **blanks** in the following sentences.

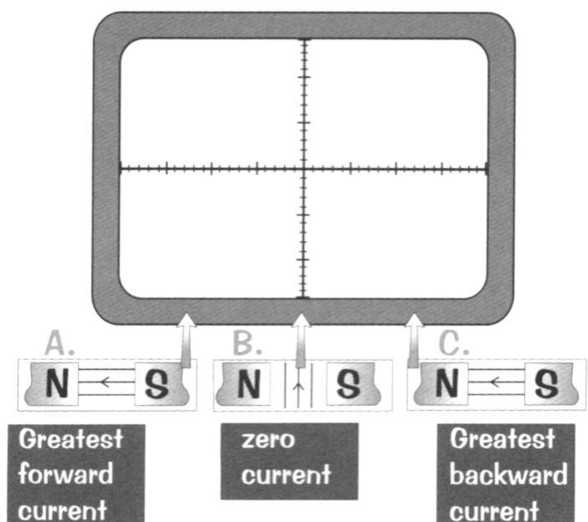


| |
|---|
| A. The current is __________ when the coil is __________ . The coil __________ magnetic field lines most __________ in this position. |
| B. The current is __________ when the coil is __________ . The coil does not cut __________ lines in this position. |
| C. Once again, the current is greatest when the coil is horizontal. |

Use these words:
***field, cuts, horizontal, vertical, zero, greatest, rapidly***

**Q8** **Give three ways** a generator could be altered to produce more current.

**Q9** *Below is data about a small lab generator, a generator in a power station, and a dynamo.*

| | |
|---|---|
| **a)** Uses a spinning electromagnet instead of a permanent magnet. | **e)** Uses a stationary permanent magnet . |
| **b)** Uses a permanent magnet which rotates. | **f)** Produces alternating current, AC. |
| **c)** Generates a current of 20,000A at a voltage of 25,000V. | **g)** Producing direct current, DC. |
| **d)** Generates a current less than 1A. | **h)** Has a magnet spinning at 50 times a second. |
| | **i)** Has a magnet spinning at variable speeds. |

**Draw a table** with the columns: *"lab generator", "power station generator" and "dynamo".* Write out the data in the correct column. *You can use the data once, more than once or not at all.*

## Top Tips

Electromagnetic induction **is** really weird, but it isn't that difficult to learn the definition: The creation of a **voltage** (and current) in a wire placed in a **changing magnetic field. Four** factors affect the size of the induced voltage, and yep, you need to learn them.

# Transformers

**Q1** *A model train is connected to the mains supply via a transformer. The following information is on the back of the transformer...*

| | | | |
|---|---|---|---|
| Input: | 230V | 50Hz | 12W |
| Output: | 12V | 1A | 12W |

a) What is the **function** of this transformer?

b) Is this a **step-up** or a **step-down** transformer? Explain your answer.

c) What is the frequency of the **mains** supply?

d) **State** what the symbols V, Hz, A and W stand for. Also, state what they are the **units** for.

**Q2** *There are 2 step-up and 2 step-down transformers here.* **Which is which?** *(The primary column is on the left and the secondary on the right).*

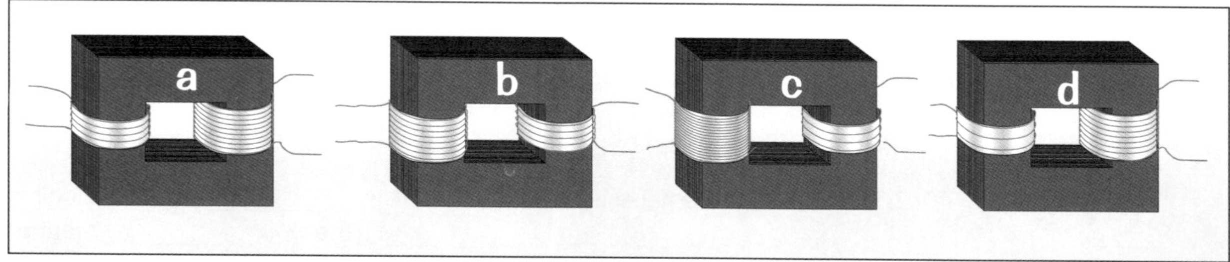


**Q3** *This table shows the number of turns on the above transformers, and the input voltage.* Find the **output voltage** in each case.

| Transformer | a | b | c | d |
|---|---|---|---|---|
| Input turns | 5 | 8 | 16 | 3 |
| Output turns | 10 | 4 | 4 | 9 |
| Input voltage | 230 | 230 | 24 | 24 |
| Output voltage | | | | |

**Q4** *This table shows the input and output voltages and the number of turns on the input coil.*

| Transformer | t | u | x | y |
|---|---|---|---|---|
| Input voltage | 180 | 230 | 12 | 20 |
| Output voltage | 9 | 23 | 180 | 50 |
| Input turns | 400 | 100 | 9 | 16 |
| Output turns | | | | |

a) Complete the table above.

b) Which of the transformers; t, u, x and y are **step-up** transformers?

c) Which of the transformers has a ratio of turns 10:1?

d) Which of the transformers has the **greatest number** of output turns?

# Transformers

**Q5** *A 9V radio takes a current of 2A. The supply to the radio is from a transformer connected to a 230V mains.*

**a)** What is the **ratio** of turns on the input and output coils of this transformer?

**b)** What is the **power** used by: **i)** the radio **ii)** the mains?

**c)** What **current** is taken by the mains?

**Q6** *This is the diagram of part of a burglar system.*

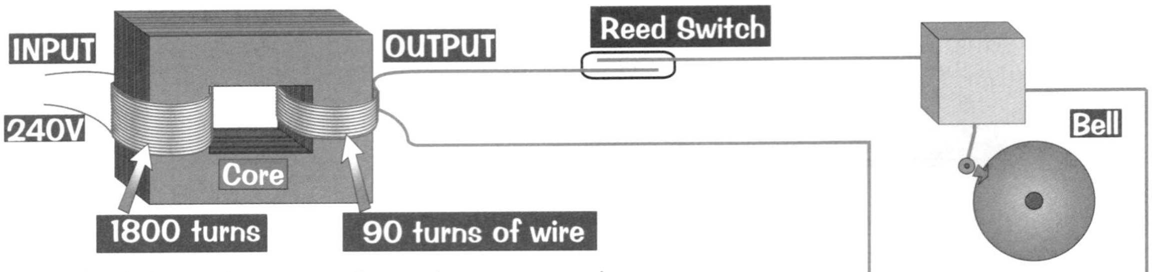


**a)** Use the information to work out the **output** voltage.

**b)** **Explain carefully** how a voltage is produced in the secondary coil.

**Q7** *Step-up transformers are used to transmit electricity at high voltage over long distances.*

Explain how this reduces the **energy losses**.

**Q8** *This question is about the transformers between power stations and peoples' homes.*

**Work out** the ratio of input : output voltage for each transformer 1-3.
Write down if a step-up or step-down transformer is needed.

**Q9** **a)** Complete the table opposite for the transformers e, f, g and h.

**b)** Find the **power output** for each of the transformers e, f, g and h.

| Transformer | e | f | g | h |
|---|---|---|---|---|
| Voltage (Primary) | 24 | 230 | 12 | |
| Current (Primary) | 1 | 2 | 3 | 0.5 |
| Voltage (Secondary) | 6 | | 6 | 6 |
| Current (Secondary) | | 1 | | 1.5 |

**Q10** **Explain** the following terms used to describe transformers:

**a)** Laminated iron core **b)** Eddy currents **c)** Magnetic field **d)** Electromagnetic induction

**e)** Primary coil **f)** Secondary coil **g)** Ratio **h)** Reversing

**Q11** **Explain why** we can not get transformers to work with DC (direct current).

## Top Tips

This is the formula you need to learn — it goes either way up.

$$\frac{\text{Primary voltage}}{\text{Secondary voltage}} = \frac{\text{Number of turns on Primary}}{\text{Number of turns on Secondary}}$$

# Mass, Weight and Gravity

**Q1** Fill in the **gaps**:

Use these words: ***bodies, large, attraction, weak, strong, field, centre, newtons, weight***

Gravity is the force of ______________ between ___________. Between objects on Earth, it is a ______________ force, but if the mass is very ___________ as with a planet or a star, the gravity can be very ________________. The region where a gravitational force can be felt is often referred to as a gravitational __________________.
The Earth's gravitational field attracts every object on Earth. This gives an object a _______________. Weight is measured in _______________, and always acts towards the ___________ of the Earth.

**Q2** *"Mass and weight" are used in everyday language almost as if they were the same thing.*

Draw a table with 2 columns, one headed "**mass**" and the other "**weight**".
Decide which information belongs to which column, and write them in:

- amount of matter
- measured in newtons
- measured by a balance
- not a force
- measured by a spring balance
- is a force
- caused by the pull of gravity
- same anywhere in the universe
- measured in kilograms
- is lower on the moon than on Earth

**Q3 a)** *"A bag of flour weighs one kilogram".*
Explain why this statement is not accurate.

**b)** Rewrite the above statement so that it is accurate.

**c)** **Complete** the table opposite for a range of masses on Earth (g = 10 N/kg).

| Mass (g) | Mass (kg) | Weight (N) |
|---|---|---|
| 5 | | |
| 10 | | |
| 100 | | |
| 200 | | |
| 500 | | |
| 1000 | | |
| 5000 | | |

**Q4** *The strength of gravity on Earth is g = 10 N/kg.* Find the **weight** of rocks with the following masses:

**a)** 5kg **b)** 10kg **c)** 2.5kg

Find the **mass** of rocks with the following weights on Earth:

**d)** 30N **e)** 150N **f)** 450N

**Q5** *The strength of gravity on the Moon is g = 1.6 N/kg.*
Find the **weight** of moon rocks with the following masses:

**a)** 5kg **b)** 10kg **c)** 2.5kg

Find the **mass** of rocks with the following weights on the Moon:

**d)** 16N **e)** 80N **f)** 960N

# Moments: Turning Forces

**Q1** For each of the seesaws **a)** to **d)**, write down if it is balanced or unbalanced.

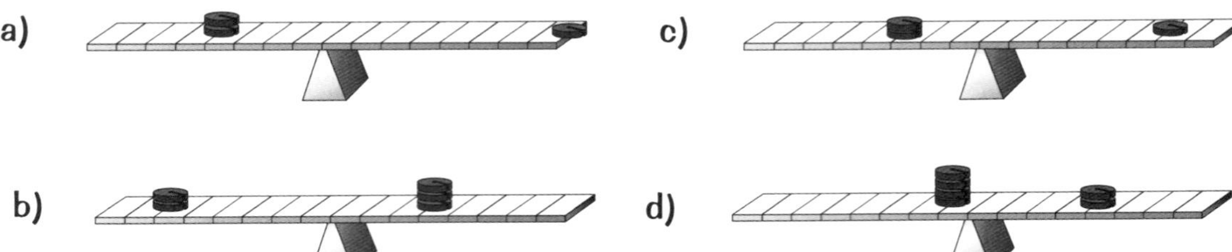


**Q2** For each of the seesaws A to D, calculate the clockwise and the anti-clockwise moment, and state whether the seesaw is balanced or unbalanced.

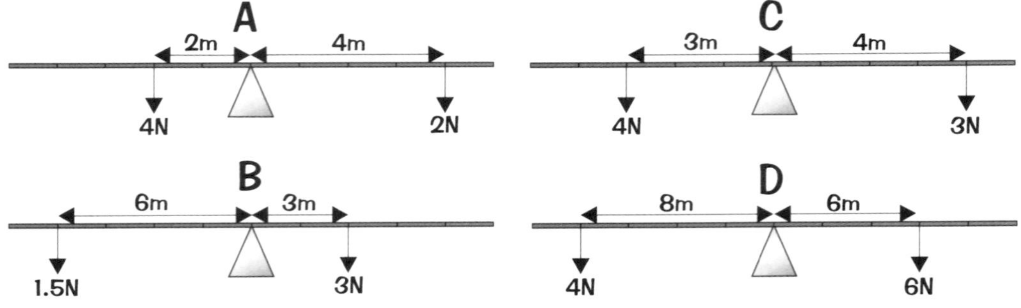


**Q3** The diagrams **i)** to **iv)** show four thin rods pivoted at X with forces applied at various distances from X

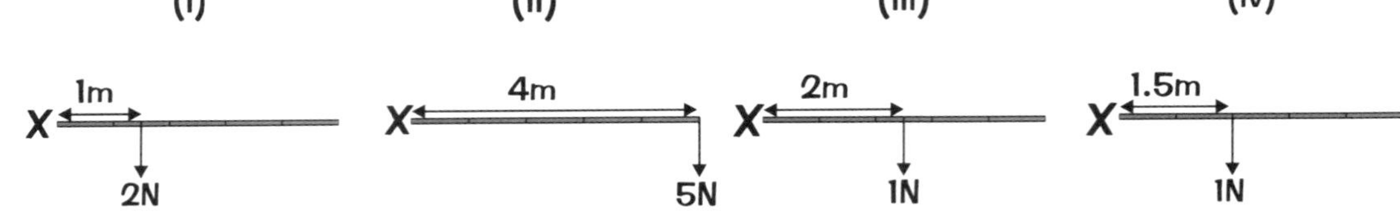


**a)** Which rod has the largest moment about the pivot X ?

**b)** Which rod has the smallest moment about the pivot X ?

**c)** Which 2 rods have an equal moment about the pivot X ?

**Q4** For the seesaws below, work out the total **clockwise** moment and total **anticlockwise** moment. **Which way** will the seesaws tip — to the left or to the right?

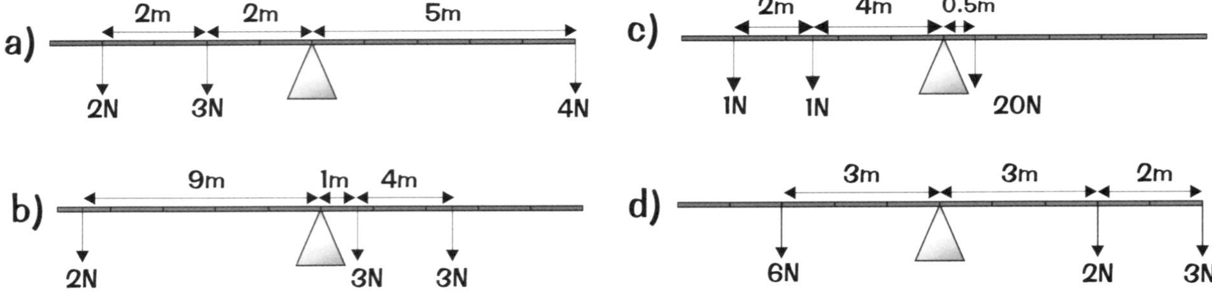


**Q5** A load of 100N is placed on a thin, light rod 4m from the pivot. **What force** do you need to apply 2m from the pivot on the opposite side to **counterbalance** the load ?

# More Moments

**Q6 a)** What is the weight of the paving stone if its mass is 50 kg? *(taking the pull of the Earth to be 10 N/kg)*

**b)** If the total length of the metal bar is 2.0m, what is the minimum force you need to apply at the other end of the metal bar to lift the paving stone?

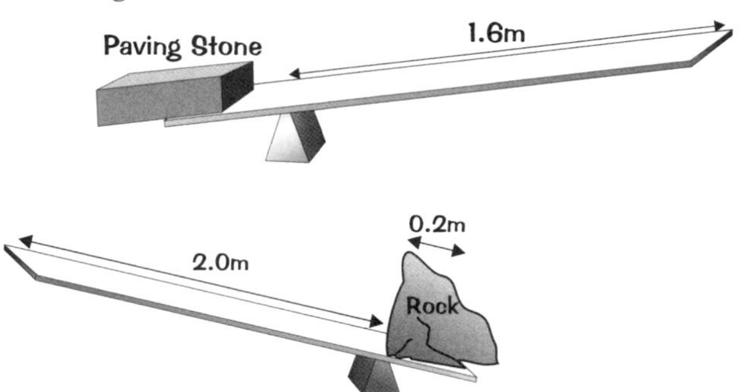


**Q7** Look at the diagram on the right. Find the minimum force which must be used to lift the rock, which has a weight of 800N.

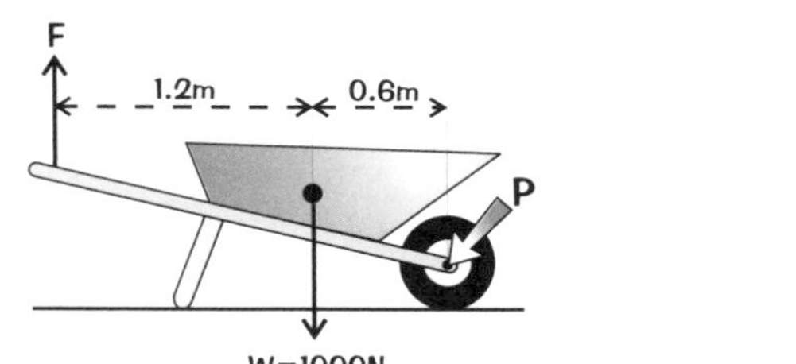


**Q8** *Point P marks the pivot point on the wheelbarrow.*

Take moments about P to find the vertical force, F, that needs to be applied to the handles of the wheelbarrow to just lift it off the ground.

F
1.2m
0.6m
P
W=1000N

**Q9** Sally is handing over an overdue book to a librarian. The book has a mass of 2kg.

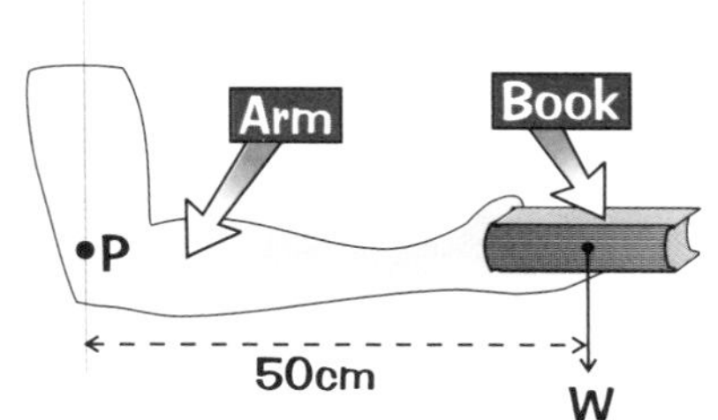


**a)** Find the weight, W, of the book.

**b)** Copy the diagram and draw an arrow for the vertical force, T, needed to support the book in this position (think carefully about where this force will be acting).

**c)** Calculate the moment of the book's weight about the pivot, P.

**Q10 a)** Look at the diagram on the right. What's the reading on the two spring balances if the two readings are equal?

**b)** If four spring balances were used with the same 1 Kg block, what reading on each balance would you get if the values are again equal?

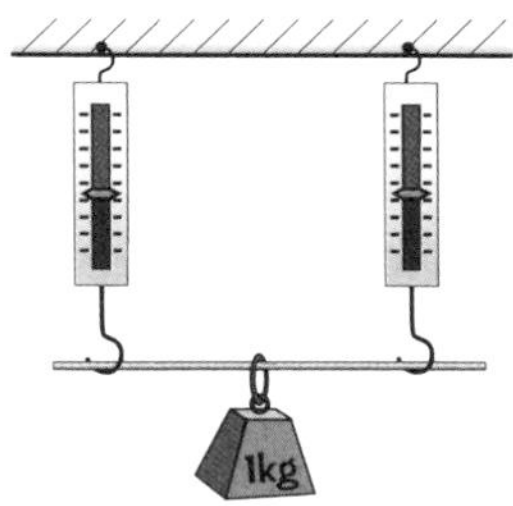


**Q11** Find the force X to be applied on the left side of the plank to balance it.

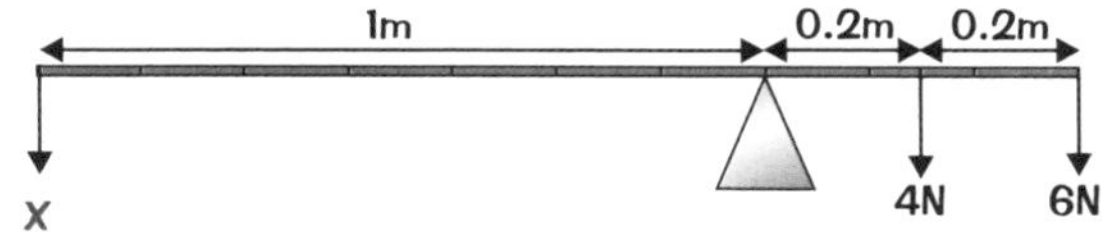


**Q12** Find the force Y to be applied on the right side of the plank to balance it.

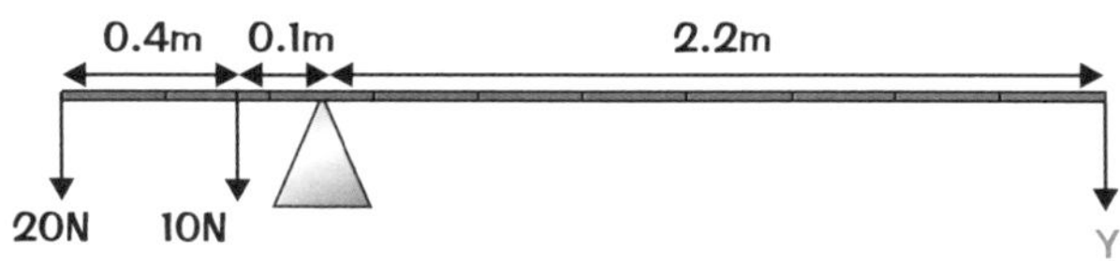


## Top Tips

Lots of tedious seesaw questions, I know, but you need plenty of practice with these. When a force acts on something which has a pivot, then you have a moment, which is a turning force making the thing rotate about its pivot. The equation you need to learn is Moment = Force × perpendicular distance, which makes sense if you think about pushing an open door near the hinge or near the handle.

# Force Diagrams

**Q1** Identify these different forces:

| | |
|---|---|
| a) Acts straight downwards. | TENSION |
| b) Slows things down. | GRAVITY or WEIGHT |
| c) In a rope or cable. | LIFT |
| d) Due to an aeroplane wing. | THRUST or PUSH or PULL |
| e) Speeds something up. | REACTION FORCE |
| f) Acts straight upwards on a horizontal plane. | DRAG or AIR RESISTANCE or FRICTION |

**Q2** *This question concerns a stationary object — a mug of tea.*

a) Copy the diagram and draw in the 2 vertical forces. Label them.

b) Explain how you know that this pair of forces is equal.

c) What would happen if there was only one vertical force?

**Q3** *A fish is hanging on the end of a fishing line.*

Copy the diagram and draw in the 2 vertical forces. Label them.

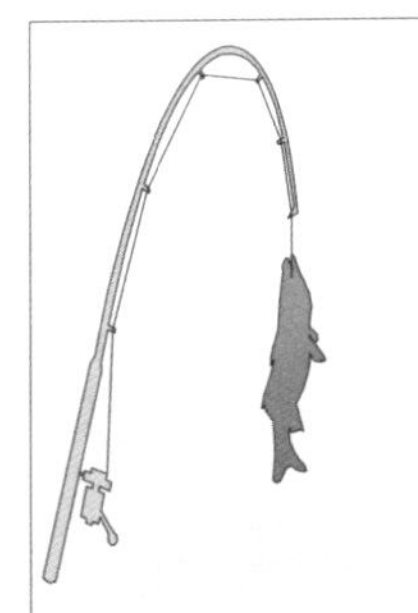

**Q4** *A car is moving forward with a steady horizontal velocity.*

a) Copy the diagram and draw in the two vertical forces. Label them.

b) Draw in the two horizontal forces. Is one force bigger than the other?

**Q5** *Rifle shooting and rocket engines provide forward motion.*

a) Draw diagrams to show the forces occurring during the firing of each (don't worry about drawing the rifle and rocket).

b) Why does a rifle "kick back" when it is fired?

**Q6** *After jumping out of an aeroplane, a skydiver accelerates until he reaches a steady vertical velocity, known as the terminal velocity.*

Draw in the two vertical forces for when the diver is at terminal velocity, and label them.

**Q7** Complete the following sentences using the words below:

drag constant stationary downwards
equilibrium weight gravity

If all forces acting on an object are in __________ , the object is either __________ or moving with a __________ velocity. The force of __________ acting upon an object (giving it a __________ ) points __________. If the object is falling through the air, another force called __________ acts in the opposite direction.

# Force Diagrams

**Q8** Study these diagrams of a submarine which is horizontal. The forces acting on the submarine are represented by arrows such that the length of the arrow is proportional to the size of the force. If the submarine starts from a constant velocity, state for each case if it will accelerate up/down/forwards/backwards or remain at that velocity. One example is done for you.

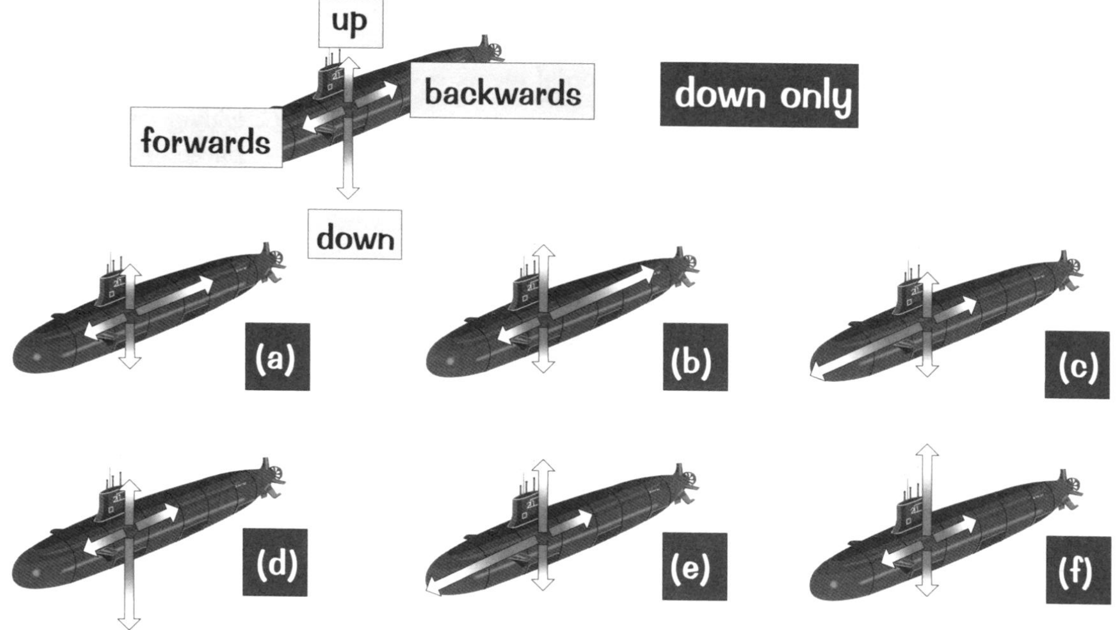


**Q9** Look at the objects **a)** to **d)** with forces applied to them as indicated by the arrows. In this question all the forces are equal.

For each object, state if it accelerates up, down, gains an angular acceleration or gains no acceleration.

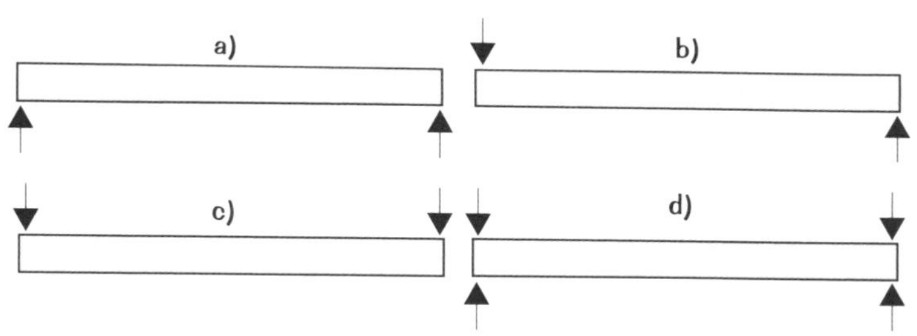


**Q10** **Complete** the following sentences with the words below:

*unbalanced faster greater greater thrust upwards*

*downwards weight reaction drag drag force smaller*

Acceleration means getting ___________. You only get acceleration with an overall resultant (___________) force. The ___________ the unbalanced ___________ the ___________ the acceleration. The ___________ the unbalanced force, the smaller the acceleration. A car which is accelerating forward has a larger ___________ than ___________ force, but the vertical forces (___________ and ___________) are the same. A skydiver accelerating ___________ has a weight force downwards, but less ___________

## Top Tips

More force questions to enjoy, this time with pictures, wow. Seriously, though, you **really do** need to be able to draw a diagram showing **all** the forces acting on an object. Don't forget to include **pairs** of forces in **equilibrium**. Remember all the forces in Question 1 — these are the only six you need to know about.

# Friction

**Q1** a) If an object is stationary and has no forces acting on it, **what happens**?

b) If an object is moving at a steady speed over a rough surface and has no forces propelling it along, **what happens**?

c) To continue travelling at a steady speed across a rough surface, **what** does an object need and **why**?

**Q2** **Match the words and the meanings**:

| | |
|---|---|
| **a)** On a car, to grip the road. | sliding friction |
| **b)** Continue moving with little grip (after braking too hard). | parachute |
| **c)** Shaped to overcome friction. | tyres |
| **d)** Increases drag in the air. | streamlined |
| **e)** Essential if a car is to stop safely. | skid |
| **f)** Friction between solid surfaces which are gripping. | brakes |
| **g)** Friction between solid surfaces which are sliding past each other. | static friction |

**Q3** **State whether** friction should be **as low as possible** or **as high as possible** in each of the following cases:

a) a car tyre in contact with the road surface.

b) a skydiver falling through the air.

c) a wheel spinning on its axle.

d) a skater moving over the ice.

e) a diver hitting the surface of the water.

f) brake blocks pressing against the rim of a bike wheel.

g) sledging in the snow.

h) climbing a mountain using a rope.

**Q4** *This diagram shows how the force of friction can be measured.*

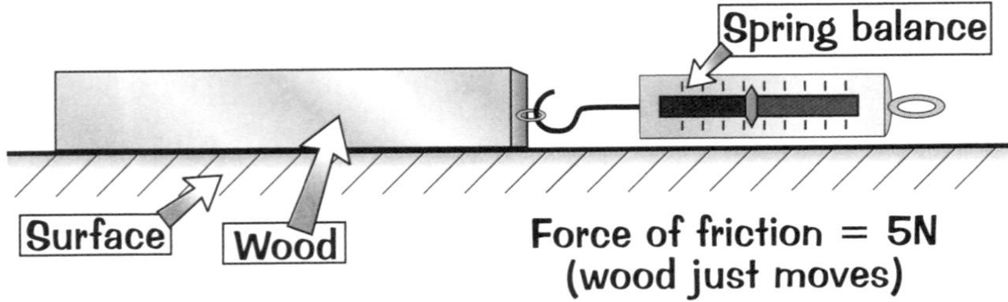


a) Give two ways you can **increase** the force of friction.

b) Give two ways of **decreasing** the friction.

**Q5** **Why** do:

a) Skiers wax their skis?

b) Machines have to be lubricated by oil?

c) Climbers wear rubber-soled shoes?

d) Ballroom dancers wear leather-soled shoes and dance on a highly polished floor?

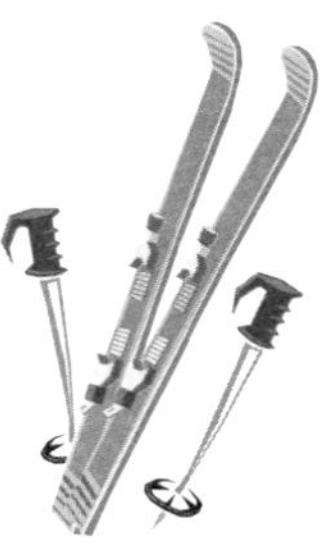

# Friction

**Q6** *Riding a bicycle gives us plenty of examples of friction being useful and a nuisance.* Divide these up into **"useful"** and **"nuisance"** and **explain** your decision each time.

| | | | |
|---|---|---|---|
| air resistance | saddle | handlebar grips | |
| pedals | wheel bearings | tyres | brakes |

**Q7** **Put these sentences into their correct sequence**:

— compared to 30 mph
— A car has much more friction
— than it would going just as far at 30 mph
— It therefore uses more petrol
— just to maintain a steady speed
— as the speed increases
— to work against when travelling at 70 mph
— So at 70 mph the engine has to work much harder
— Air resistance always increases

**Q8** *Friction causes wear and heating.* Answer these questions about these **two** effects of friction.

**a)** **Give three examples** where friction acts between surfaces that are **sliding** over each other.

**b)** Friction produces **heat** energy. Give two examples where this is **useful**.

**c)** What can be used to keep friction in **machinery** as **low** as possible?

**d)** Explain what will happen to an engine running without oil?

**e)** **Explain** why brakes might need to be replaced more often for a racing car than for a car that is only used around town (30 mph speed limit).

**Q9** *Suppose someone invented a frictionless material.*

Which of the following would be **impossible** to do with it, and **why**:

**a)** Run across a thin sheet of it.

**b)** Slide across a sheet of it.

**c)** Stop sliding across a sheet of it.

Which of the following would be **useful** if made out of it:

**d)** Nuts and bolts.

**e)** Tables.

**f)** Tyres.

**g)** Car bodies.

**h)** Roofs.

## Top Tips

Friction is always there to slow things down — you can't afford to ignore it, so learn all the stuff on these pages. Remember the **three** ways that friction occurs — solids gripping each other, solids sliding past each other and drag from fluids. And don't forget that friction can be **helpful** as well as a **nuisance**. Lastly, because friction causes wear and heating, machinery needs **oil** to **lubricate** it and stop it from wearing down — or **even worse**, welding itself together from the extreme heat.

# The Three Laws of Motion

**Q1** *Newton's First Law of Motion states that balanced forces means no change in velocity.*

a) **Explain clearly** the underlined terms (balanced forces and velocity).

b) **Draw a diagram** of something (a car, bus, stick man) moving at a constant velocity. **Draw in** the horizontal forces.

c) **Describe** what is meant by the term "resultant" force.

d) For your diagram in b) **what** is the resultant force?

**Q2** a) **Draw a diagram** of a submarine with the forces acting on it, if it's resting on the ocean bed.

b) **What** is the velocity of the submarine?

**Q3** Newton's Second Law of Motion states that a non-zero resultant force means acceleration.

Complete the following sentences about this law, using the words below.

force unequal slowing down speeding up stopping
accelerate decelerate direction starting

> If there is an unbalanced ____________ , then an object will ____________ or ____________ in that ____________ . This change in motion can take five different forms: ____________ , ____________ , ____________ ____________ , ____________ ____________ and changing direction. On a force diagram, the arrows will be ____________ .

**Q4** Answer TRUE or FALSE. **Explain** your answer.

a) "If something is moving, there must be an overall force on it".

b) "You get steady speed from balanced forces".

c) "You get acceleration/deceleration if there is an overall force acting on an object".

d) "The bigger the force, the smaller the acceleration".

e) "The bigger the mass, the smaller the acceleration".

f) "To get a small mass to accelerate as much as a big mass, it needs a bigger force".

**Q5** a) In the equation F = ma, **explain** what F, m and a stand for.

b) **What** are the units of F, m and a?

c) **Rearrange** the equation as "a = ".

d) **Rearrange** the equation as "m = ".

**Q6** **Fill in the gaps:**

Use the following words: force, acceleration, mass, one newton, mass, double

> To give a ____________ of 1 kilogram an ____________ of 1 metre per second squared, a force of ______ ________ is needed. Twice the ____________ pushing on the same ____________ would produce ____________ the acceleration.

**Q7** Find the **force** acting on these objects:

a) mass 10kg, acceleration 5 $m/s^2$.

b) mass 50kg, acceleration 2.5 $m/s^2$.

c) mass 400kg, acceleration 8 $m/s^2$.

# The Three Laws of Motion

**Q8** **Find** the acceleration of these objects:

**a)** Resultant Force 100N, mass 10kg.

**b)** Resultant Force 500N, mass 25kg.

**c)** Resultant Force 75N, mass 2.5kg.

**d)** *One of the above objects is falling towards Earth.* **Which one** is it?

**Q9**

| (i) | (ii) | (iii) | (iv) |
|---|---|---|---|
| 2kg → 4N | 1kg → 3N | 4kg → 8N | 1.5kg → 3N |

**a)** Which masses have the same accelerations?

**b)** Which has the biggest acceleration?

**c)** Which has the smallest acceleration?

**Q10** *An astronaut, who weighs 900N on Earth, climbs into his space craft and takes off. Once in orbit, he engages his super thrust booster engines which, according to 'Which Interstellar Spaceship?' magazine, has a maximum output force of 60 million newtons. He accelerates from 0 to 60 (that's 60 km/sec) in 10 seconds. Checking his copy of 'Which Interstellar Spaceship?', he finds that the figure for the mass of his craft is smudged.*

Can you **work out** what it is?

**Q11** *When Sarah is sitting in her go-cart, the total mass is 50kg. Starting from rest at the top of a hill, she experiences a force of 100N down the hill, and a constant resistance of 10N in the opposite direction. She sets off with a tiny push, and travels for ten seconds before the hill levels off.*

**What** is her **velocity** when she reaches the bottom?

**Q12** *This question is about Newton's Third Law of Motion.*

**a)** **State** the law. **Start off with** "If object A exerts a force on object B then .....".

**b)** **Explain** what happens when you push on a wall, in terms of Newton's Third Law. **Draw a diagram** to explain your answer. Include the forces.

**c)** If an object is on a horizontal surface, **what force** will there be pushing upwards?

**d)** **What** other force acting on the object is this force equal to?

**e)** **Draw a diagram** which illustrates your answers to both **c)** and **d)**.

**Q13** *A circus cannon is fired, giving Coco the Clown an acceleration of 5 $m/s^2$. He has a mass of 90kg.*

**a)** What force propelled Coco?

**b)** What force is exerted on the cannon?

**c)** If the cannon has a mass of 450kg, how fast will it accelerate, and in what direction?

## Top Tips

The three laws are the basic facts you need to understand forces and motion. Learn them and understand them — they're pretty **simple**, don't get caught out saying something **totally stupid**, like "if something's moving there must be an overall force acting on it". That's wrong, really really wrong.

# Speed and Velocity

**Q1** *Getting going!* **How fast is:**

**a)** An athlete who runs 100m (metres) in 10s (seconds)?

**b)** A racing car zooming 240m in 12s?

**c)** A student, walking 600m in 240s?

**d)** A tortoise with a twisted ankle, shuffling 10m in 100s?

**Q2** *Keeping going....*

**a)** *Sir misses a paper aeroplane thrown from the middle of the classroom, which is 5m away. It takes 1.5 seconds to reach him.* **What** is its speed? **How long** would it have taken to reach him if it had been thrown from the back row of desks, 10m away?

**b)** *A snail creeps 1m in 500s.* **What** is its speed?

**c)** **Find** the speed of a rocket zooming 280,000m in 20s. What is this speed in km/s?

**Q3** *How long?*

**a)** *Your flashy neighbour reckons his new racing bike can reach 18 m/s.* He finished 10 laps of 120m track in 70s. **Work out** his speed. **Could** he be telling porky pie **lies**?

**b)** *A sprinter crosses the 100m race finish line.* His speed throughout the race was 10 m/s so **how long** did it take him?

**c)** *The greyhound racetrack is 750m long.* If Droopy's speed is 25 m/s, **what** is his time?

**Q4** *How far?*

**a)** **How far** around the track would a racing car get, going at 90 m/s for 30s ?

**b)** *Concorde's travelling across the sky at 650 m/s.* **How far** can it go in 25s, travelling at this speed?

**c)** **Find** how far a cheetah could get if its speed is 30 m/s (70 mph) and it runs for 500s.

**d)** **How far** would a roadrunner go travelling at a speed of 25 m/s (56 mph) in 700s.

**Q5** *Speed and velocity! Remember that speed is how fast you're going, and velocity has direction. If you change direction, you change velocity, even if the speed stays the same.*

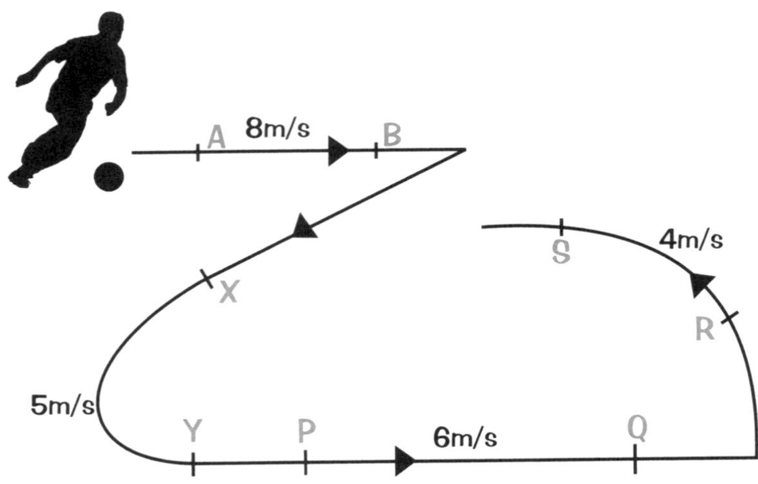


Between points A and B, X and Y, P and Q, S and R Ronaldo moves with the constant speeds shown. Between which of these points has he also constant velocity?

# Speed and Velocity

**Q6** Complete the sentences:

Use these words: ***fast, direction, how, direction***

Speed is ___________ ___________ you're going with no regard to ___________.
Velocity, however, must also have the ___________ specified.

**Q7** Divide these into 3 columns — "Units of speed", "Units of velocity" and "Other units":

m/s   m/s WEST   m   s
m/s NORTH   mph

**Q8** *A cat skulks 50m in 90s.* Find:

**a)** its speed.

**b)** how long it takes to go 120m.

**Q9** *A car travels 600m in 30s.*

**a)** Find its average speed.

**b)** *The car's* average speed is usually different from its speed at any particular instant in time? Explain the reason for this.

**c)** How far would the car travel at the same speed in 1500s?

**Q10** Find the speed (in m/s) of:

**a)** a train going 1200km in 8 hours.

**b)** a walker who travels 12km in 2½ hours.

**Q11** How far does:

**a)** a cyclist travel in 3 hours at an average speed of 12 km/h?

**b)** a ship travel in 5 hours at an average speed of 25 km/h?

**Q12** How long does it take:

**a)** a car to cover 560km at an average speed of 70 km/h?

**b)** light to travel from the Sun to the Earth (150,000,000 km) at a speed of 300,000 km/s? (answer in minutes and seconds).

**Q13** Find the velocity of a car travelling 2000m due North in 100s.

**Q14** Find the velocity of a walker travelling a distance of 1000m East in 500s.

**Q15** Find the velocity of a bird flying 450m South-East in 5s.

**Q16** *A walker starts in Barchester at 10am. He walks 5km North-East to Histon, getting there at 11am. He takes a half-hour break, then walks back to Barchester in 50 minutes.*

**a)** What is his velocity (in m/s) when walking to Histon?

**b)** What is his velocity when walking back to Barchester?

**c)** What is his average speed for the whole trip?

## Top Tips

Speed and velocity, they're not the same. Speed and velocity are both how fast you're going, measured in m/s (or km/h or mph), but velocity also has to specify the direction e.g. 30m/s north. Remember Speed = Distance/Time. If you write it as a formula triangle it makes things a whole lot easier.

# Acceleration

**Q1** **a)** In the equation $\mathbf{a} = \frac{\Delta V}{\Delta t}$ state **what** a, ΔV and Δt **stand for**.

**b)** State the usual **units** of a, ΔV and Δt.

**c)** **Explain** how acceleration is different from speed and velocity.

**Q2** **Complete these sentences**:

Use these words: ***acceleration, second, 3 m/s, second, acceleration, 4 m/s, velocity, velocity***

**a)** A motorbike has a steady __________ of 3 m/s². This means that every __________ its __________ changes by __________.

**b)** A car has a steady __________ of 4 m/s². This means that every __________ its __________ changes by __________.

**Q3** Complete the charts showing steady acceleration and deceleration.

| Time (s) | 1 | 2 | 3 | 4 | 5 | 6 |
|---|---|---|---|---|---|---|
| Speed X (m/s) | 2.0 | 4.0 | 6.0 | | 10.0 | |
| Speed Y (m/s) | 17.5 | 15.0 | 12.5 | | 7.5 | |

What is the **acceleration** of X?
What is the **deceleration** of Y? **How** can you tell that it is decelerating?

**Q4** **Find** the acceleration of:

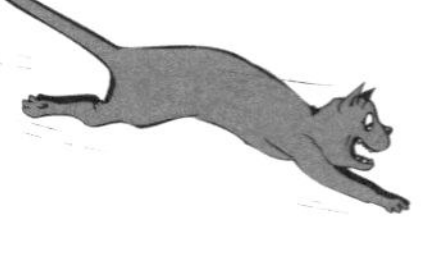

**a)** A cat, pouncing from 0 m/s to 5 m/s in 4s.

**b)** A car, speeding from 10 m/s to 30 m/s in 5s.

**c)** A runner, going from 3 m/s to 8 m/s in 3s.

**Q5** *A car has a steady acceleration of 2 m/s².* If it starts from rest, **what's its velocity** after 10s?

**Q6** What is the deceleration of a car that takes 8s for its speed to drop from 20 m/s to 0 m/s?

**Q7** How long does a motorbike take to stop if it's travelling at a speed of 16 m/s and then **decelerates** at a rate of 2 m/s²?

**Q8** *PC Bacon is cruising along in his car at 15 m/s.*

**a)** *He keeps on going for an hour.*
**How far** does he go, in kilometres?

**b)** *A car shoots past at 80 mph. One mile is about 1.6 kilometres.*
How fast is the car going in kilometres per hour, and in metres per second?

**c)** *PC Bacon gives chase, and accelerates steadily at 1 m/s² up to 40 m/s.*
**How long** does this take?

**d)** *After travelling along for 3 minutes at 40m/s, he catches up with the speeding car.* **How far** has he travelled since reaching 40 m/s?

**e)** *The speeding car is now travelling at 28 m/s. PC Bacon flags it down, and it pulls over into a layby.* If it takes 15s to halt, **what** is its deceleration?

# Acceleration

**Q9** *This question is about a car whose motion is described by a velocity/time graph.*

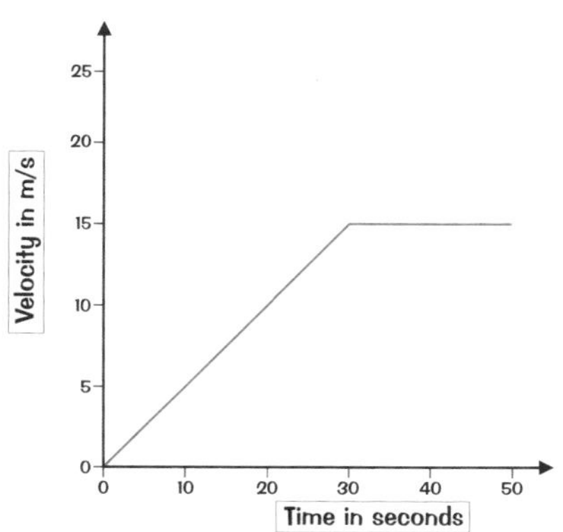


a) **How far** does the car travel in the first 30 seconds?

b) **Describe** the motion of the car in the next 20 seconds.

c) **Copy** the graph with the time axis extended to 100 seconds and **complete** the graph using the following information:

(i) between the times of 50 and 60 seconds, the car undergoes a steady acceleration to 20 m/s.

(ii) for the next 20 seconds the car's speed is steady at 20 m/s.

(iii) during the next 20 seconds, the car slows to a stop at a steady rate.

d) **Calculate** the acceleration occurring in c) (i).

e) **Calculate** the deceleration occurring in c) (iii).

f) **Work out** the distance travelled during the last 40 seconds of this short trip.

**Q10** *This question is about the motion of a motorbike described by a distance/time graph.*

a) **What** is the **maximum** speed of the motor bike?

b) **What distance** does the motor bike travel in the first 20 seconds?

c) **Calculate** the motor bike's speed between 20 and 40 seconds.

d) **Describe carefully** how the motor bike moves during the 60 seconds (use words like accelerates, decelerates, steady speed).

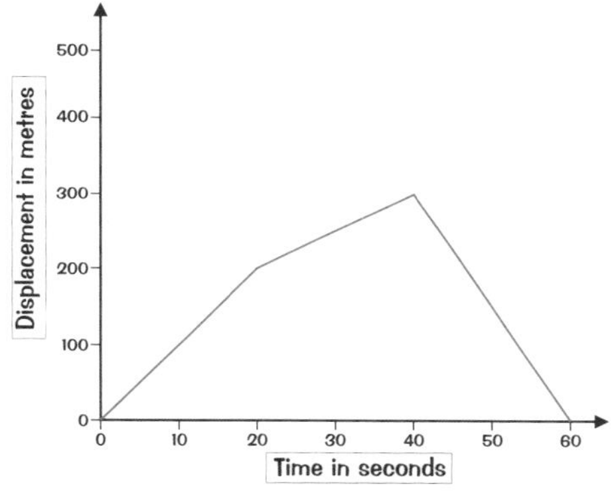


**Q11** *Here's another question about a car moving.*

| Velocity (m) | Time (s) |
|---|---|
| 0 | 0 |
| 0 | 1 |
| 9 | 2 |
| 18 | 3 |
| 27 | 4 |
| 36 | 5 |
| 45 | 6 |
| 54 | 7 |
| 54 | 8 |
| 54 | 9 |
| 54 | 10 |

a) **Plot the graph** of velocity in m/s (vertical axis) against time in seconds (horizontal axis) but extend the time axis to 15 seconds.

b) **How quickly does the car accelerate** after it starts moving?

c) **Describe** the motion of the car between 0 and 10 seconds.

d) **What** steady deceleration is required by the car between 10 and 15 seconds to bring it to a halt at 15 seconds?

e) **Find** the total distance travelled by the car.

## Top Tips

Acceleration **isn't** the same as velocity or speed. **Acceleration** is **how fast** the **velocity** is **changing** — it's a bit more subtle. The equation to remember here is Acceleration = Change in Velocity/Time taken (use a formula triangle, it'll help). The **units** of acceleration are **$m/s^2$**, metres per second per second.

# Distance/Time and Velocity/Time Graphs

**Q1** *This question is about a distance/time graph describing the motion of a car.*

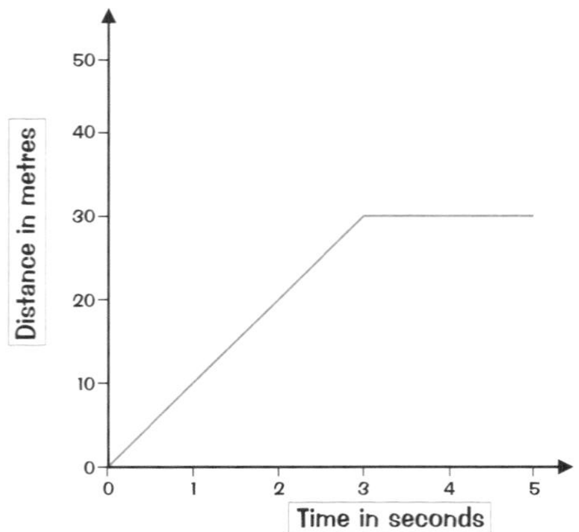


a) **How far** does the car go in 3 seconds?

b) **Find** the speed of the car during the first 3 seconds.

c) **Describe** what happens between 3 seconds and 5 seconds.

d) **Copy** the graph and **draw** a line showing the motion of a different car that, during the first 3 seconds, travels at half the speed of the original car.

**Q2** *This question is about a cyclist riding a bike.*

a) **How far** does the cyclist travel during the first 20 seconds of his journey?

b) Between the times of 20 and 40 seconds, **what is** the **deceleration** of the cyclist?

c) How far does the cyclist travel during the period of deceleration described in (b)?

d) **What happens** over the next 20 seconds of the journey?

e) What is the total distance travelled by the cyclist for the whole 60 seconds?

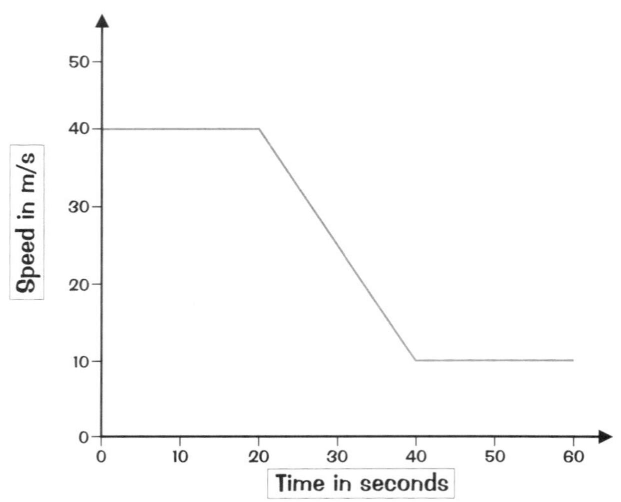


**Q3** *A car passes a crossing. Its distance from the crossing is measured every second.*

| Distance (m) | Time (s) |
|---|---|
| 0 | 0 |
| 2 | 1 |
| 9 | 2 |
| 18 | 3 |
| 27 | 4 |
| 36 | 5 |
| 45 | 6 |
| 54 | 7 |
| 54 | 8 |
| 54 | 9 |
| 54 | 10 |

a) **Plot a graph** of distance in metres (vertical axis) against time in seconds (horizontal axis).

b) Mark on the graph where the car (i) is accelerating, (ii) is travelling at a steady speed, (iii) is stopped.

c) **What** is the average speed of the car in the first 7 seconds?

d) **What distance** has the car travelled after 5.5 seconds?

e) **How long** did the car take to travel 23 metres?

# Distance/Time and Velocity/Time Graphs

**Q4** Complete the table by stating the significance of features sometimes observed on Distance/Time and Velocity/Time graphs.

| Feature on Graph | Distance/Time | Velocity/Time |
|---|---|---|
| Gradient equals | | |
| Flat sections show | | |
| Curves show | | |
| Downhill section shows | | |
| Area under the curve shows | NOT APPLICABLE | |

**Q5** Draw the velocity/time graph using these measurements taken during a car journey.

a) Describe the motion of the car (write on the graph).

b) Calculate the acceleration of the car in the first 12 seconds.

c) If the car had a mass of 1000 kilograms, what force was needed to produce the acceleration in (b)?

d) Calculate the deceleration of the car in the last 4 seconds.

| Velocity (m/s) | Time (s) |
|---|---|
| 0 | 0 |
| 4 | 2 |
| 8 | 4 |
| 12 | 6 |
| 16 | 8 |
| 20 | 10 |
| 24 | 12 |
| 24 | 14 |
| 24 | 16 |
| 12 | 18 |
| 0 | 20 |

**Q6** Draw a distance/time graph using these measurements taken during a bike journey.

| Distance (m) | Time (s) |
|---|---|
| 0 | 0 |
| 20 | 5 |
| 40 | 10 |
| 60 | 15 |
| 80 | 20 |
| 100 | 25 |
| 100 | 30 |
| 50 | 35 |
| 0 | 40 |

a) Describe the motion of the bike for the whole journey (write on the graph).

b) Calculate the speed of the bike between the times of 20 and 25 seconds.

c) For how long is the bike stationary?

d) Calculate the speed of the bike between the times of 30 and 40 seconds.

e) What is the total distance covered by the cyclist?

## Top Tips

These graphs look similar, and it would be tempting to try and avoid learning all the differences between them. Be warned, if you don't know what all the details mean and you can't distinguish between the two types of graph, then you will get all these questions wrong. Harsh but true.

# Resultant Force and Terminal Velocity

**Q1** Complete the following sentences using these words:

adding subtracting resultant forces direction overall
motion same accelerate decelerate steady

In most real situations, there are at least two forces acting on an object along any ____________ . The ____________ effect of these forces will decide the ____________ of the object — whether it will ____________ , ____________ or stay at a ____________ speed. The overall effect is found by ____________ or ____________ the forces which point along the ____________ direction. The overall force you get is a ____________ .

**Q2** *A car of mass 2,000kg has a faulty engine which provides a driving force of 5,500N at all times. At 70 mph the drag force acting on the car is 5,400N.*

a) **Draw a diagram** for both cases (rest and at 70 mph) showing the forces acting on the car. *There is no need to show vertical forces.*

b) **Find** the car's acceleration when first setting off from rest. (The drag can be neglected).

c) **Find** the car's acceleration at 70 mph.

**Q3** *A smaller car of mass 1,500kg has an engine which provides a maximum driving force of 4,500N. At 70 mph the drag force acting on the car is 4,450N.*

a) **Draw a diagram** for both cases (starting from rest and travelling at 70 mph) showing the forces acting on the car. *There is no need to show vertical forces.*

b) **Find** the car's acceleration at 70 mph if the driver's foot is to the floor.

c) **What** force is needed to accelerate the car steadily to a speed of 4 m/s in 2 seconds, if it is starting from rest? Assume the drag to be negligible.

**Q4** *This information about cars and free-fallers reaching a terminal velocity is in the wrong order.* Put the following statements in the correct order.

- the forces due to resistance.
- until eventually the resistance forces balance the accelerating forces,
- When cars and free-falling objects first set off
- at which point the cars or objects are unable to accelerate any more.
- the forces accelerating them are greater than
- As the body's velocity increases the resistance forces rise

**Q5** Consider the parachutist on the right:

a) **Copy** the diagram and **label** the two vertical forces acting on her.

b) Sketch a **velocity/time graph** showing the change in velocity of the parachutist as she falls (include the period of free fall and the period when the parachute is open). Explain the graph in terms of the forces acting on the parachutist.

**Q6** **What is another name** given to each of the following?

a) The downward force acting on falling bodies.

b) Air resistance.

c) The maximum velocity reached by a falling object.

d) A useful piece of equipment to increase air resistance.

e) A shape which will decrease air resistance.

# Resultant Force and Terminal Velocity

**Q7** **Answer true or false.**

a) A feather and a hamster will not land at the same time if dropped from the same height above the Moon.

b) Acceleration equals force times mass.

c) The drag force depends on shape and area.

d) The forces of air resistance and weight are equal when a falling object is travelling at its maximum speed (terminal velocity).

e) The speed at which weight equals air resistance is the same whether a falling sky diver has a parachute open or not.

**Q8** **Fill in the gaps**

*same* *weight* *drag* *resistance* *falling*

> The downward force acting on all ___________ objects is gravity, which would make them fall at the ___________ rate if it wasn't for air ___________ . The terminal velocity of any object is determined by its ___________ in comparison to the ___________ of it.

**Q9** **Plot the graph** of velocity (in m/s) [vertical axis] against time (in s) [horizontal axis] showing the motion of a human skydiver after jumping out of an aeroplane.

Then answer these questions:

a) **Find** the terminal velocity of the skydiver. (Be sure to give the units)

b) **Estimate** the velocity of the skydiver after:

i) 5s ii) 12.5s.

c) At what time does the skydiver reach terminal velocity?

d) The skydiver opens her parachute 20 seconds after jumping out of the aeroplane. Describe the extra force acting on her and its effect upon her speed.

e) Will the skydiver reach a new terminal velocity? **Explain** your answer.

| Velocity (m/s) | Time (s) |
|---|---|
| 0 | 0 |
| 4.5 | 2 |
| 16.5 | 4 |
| 23.0 | 6 |
| 29.0 | 8 |
| 36.0 | 10 |
| 43.5 | 12 |
| 50.0 | 14 |
| 56.0 | 16 |
| 60.0 | 18 |
| 60.0 | 20 |

**Q10** **Draw** the diagrams below showing the resultant forces. If the body is accelerating, write down the direction (up, down, right or left) in which it is accelerating.

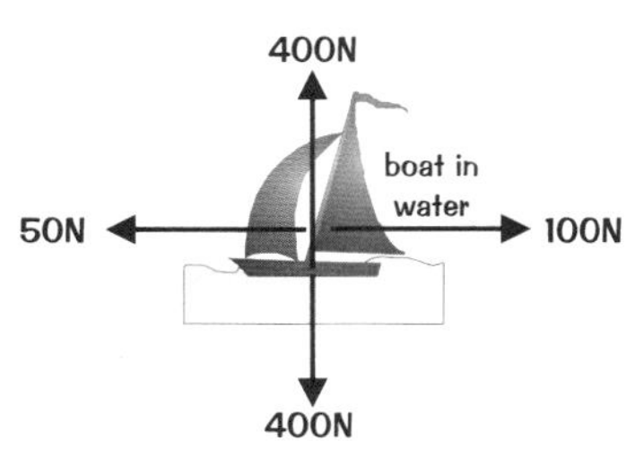

A boat in the water

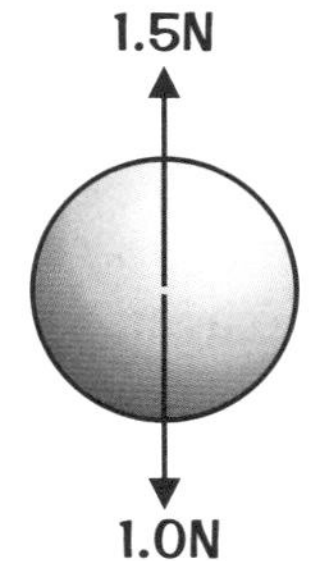

A ball being blown upwards by a jet of air

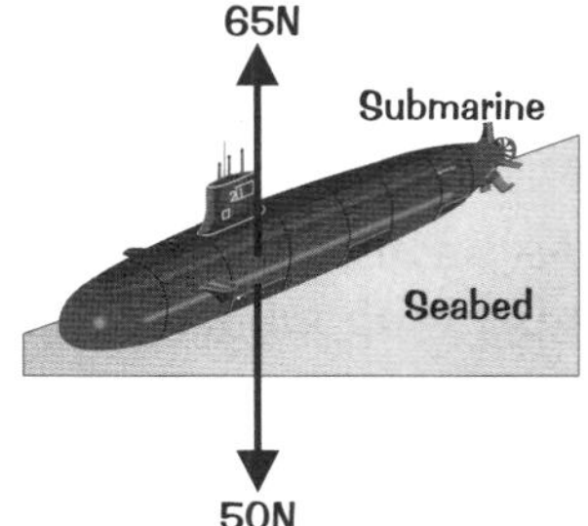

A model submarine on the sea bed

A shuttlecock in the air

## Top Tips

The idea of **Resultant Force** is really important. The resultant force is just the **overall force** acting on an object. You get it by adding or subtracting forces that act in the same direction. Obviously, it's the overall resultant force that decides if the object **accelerates**, **decelerates** or stays at a **steady speed**.

# Basic Principles of Waves

**Q1** Copy the following sentences and **fill in the gaps**.

**a)** There are two different types of wave motion: ______________ and ______________.

**b)** The number of waves per second passing a fixed point is called the ______________ and is measured in _________.

**c)** The time taken for two adjacent crests to pass a fixed point is called the___________ and is measured in __________ .

**d)** The maximum distance of particles from their resting position is called the ___________.

**e)** The highest point of a transverse wave is called a ____________.

**f)** The lowest point of a transverse wave is called a ____________.

**g)** The distance travelled each second by a wave is called its ____________ and is measured in ___________.

**h)** Waves will change their speed and wavelength when they go into different materials; this is called ______________.

**i)** Waves will spread out when they pass through a small gap; this is called ____________.

**Q2** Describe the motion of the particles in an ocean wave.

**Q3** Describe the motion of the particles in a sound wave moving through air.

**Q4** Give a definition of "wavelength". What unit is it measured in?

**Q5** What does a wave transfer?

**Q6** *You can send a wave along a piece of string by shaking one end up and down (see diagram).*

**a)** What do we call the up and down movement of the string?

**b)** How would you increase the frequency of this wave?

**c)** How would you increase its amplitude?

**d)** This wave is a transverse wave. Explain why a longitudinal wave of a similar frequency can not be made to travel along the string.

**Q7** *You are floating in the sea, measuring waves (as you do). You time 5 seconds between one crest passing and the next.*

**a)** What is the period of this wave?

**b)** What is the frequency of this wave?

**c)** *By watching the waves move along a breakwater you estimate that the distance between 10 crests is about 30m.* Calculate the average **wavelength** of the waves.

**d)** **How far** have the waves travelled each time a crest passes you?

**e)** **How long** does it take the wave to pass you?

**f)** How far does the wave travel in ONE second?

**g)** What is the **speed** of the wave?

**h)** Which way do you move as the wave passes through you?

**Q8** *A sound wave will not travel for ever.*

**a)** What happens to, a) the wavelength and b) the amplitude, if no energy is supplied to it?

**b)** What form of energy is the energy transferred into?

# Basic Principles of Waves

**Q9** There are six equations below; some of which are incorrect.

**a)** Write down the correct versions, first in words, then using the usual symbols.

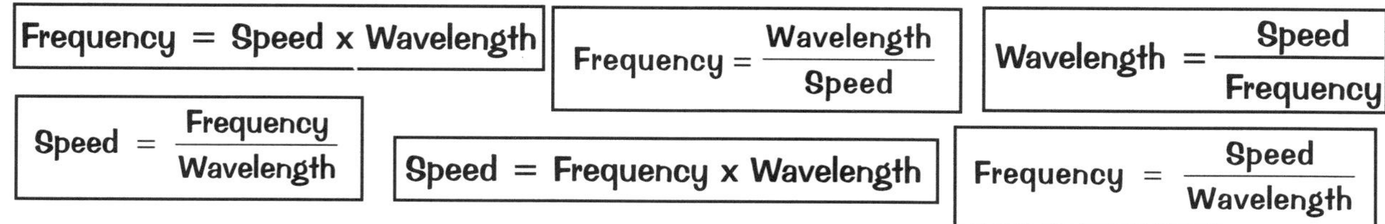


**b)** Write an equation relating a wave's period T, with its wavelength and speed.

**Q10** *The diagram below shows a piece of string with a wave travelling along it. There are beads attached to the string in positions A, B, C, D, E, F, G, H and I.*

**a)** Draw on the diagram where the stationary string would lie after the wave has died away.

**b)** Which bead(s) are:

**i)** at the crests?

**ii)** at troughs?

**iii)** moving up?

**iv)** moving down?

**v)** changing direction?

**vi)** stationary?

**vii)** moving with the greatest speed?

**viii)** moving with the greatest acceleration?

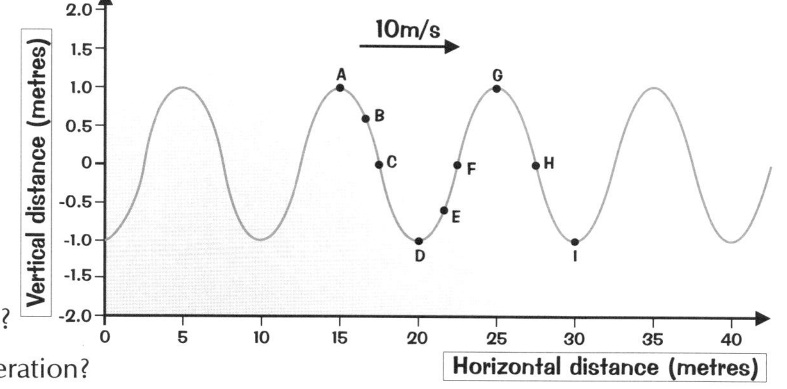


**c)** Calculate the amplitude, wavelength and frequency of the wave.

**Q11** A certain radio programme is broadcast on a wavelength of 2.250km. If the speed of radio waves is $3 \times 10^8$ m/s, calculate the frequency of the transmission.

**Q12** *A ruler was flicked on the side of a table and viewed under a rapidly flashing light (stroboscope). The time between the flashes was increased until the tip of the ruler appeared stationary. This happened when the light produced 48 pulses of light per second.*

**a)** Why did the ruler look like it was stationary under this light?

**b)** What is the period of oscillation of the ruler?

**c)** *The stroboscope flash rate is gradually decreased. The ruler appears to move again and then becomes stationary for a second time.* How many flashes per second is needed for this to happen? Explain your answer.

## Top Tip

Don't forget the difference between **transverse** and **longitudinal** waves. You'll need to be able to give three examples of each type of wave. One more thing, and that's the wave formulae — remember when you need to use them, and **watch out for the units**.

# Light Waves

**Q1** Describe how **rainbows** are formed and explain what this tells you about the *composition of sunlight*.

**Q2** Give two different methods of splitting white light into its constituent colours in the laboratory.

**Q3** **Copy and complete** the table opposite comparing red and violet light. Use the following words to fill in the gaps.

**Long, Low, Same, High, Short**

| Wave Property | Red Light | Violet Light |
|---|---|---|
| Speed | | |
| Frequency | | |
| Wavelength | | |

**Q4 a)** **Copy and complete** the diagram to show the path of the light beam through the prism and the coloured light exiting the opposite face. Label the colours in the right order.

**b)** What is the name given to this effect?

**c)** Which colour shows the largest angle of deviation?

**d)** Mark on your diagram where infra-red and ultra violet light should exit (although they are invisible).

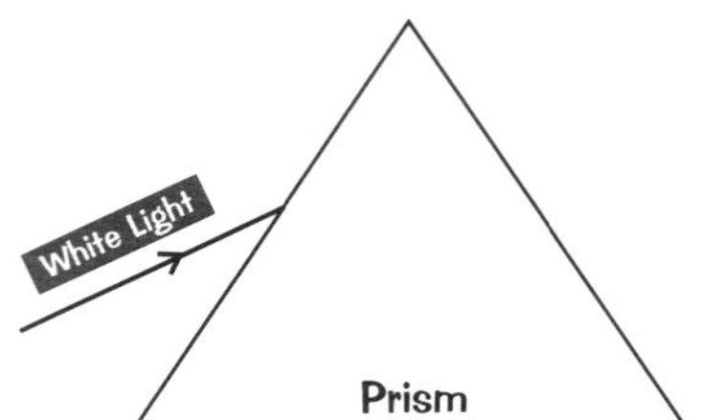


**Q5** *Getting the green light......*

**a)** What is the correct order of the colours in the visible spectrum?

**b)** **Write down** which of these sentences you think are correct.

- *Green has a longer wavelength than yellow light.*
- *Red light has a lower frequency than blue light.*
- *Increasing the frequency of green light could make it blue.*
- *Yellow light travels more slowly than violet light.*
- *Orange light has a higher frequency than red light.*

*A particular light source gives out green light. What changes in the light would you see if you increased the...*

**c)** **amplitude** of the light waves?

**d)** **frequency** of the light waves?

**e)** **wavelength** of the light waves?

**Q6** The waves A, B and C below represent red, green and violet light waves (not in that order).

**Read** the sentences below and **write down** the ones which are correct.

- *B is violet.*
- *The red light has the largest amplitude.*
- *C has the highest frequency.*
- *Green has the smallest amplitude.*
- *A has the shortest wavelength.*

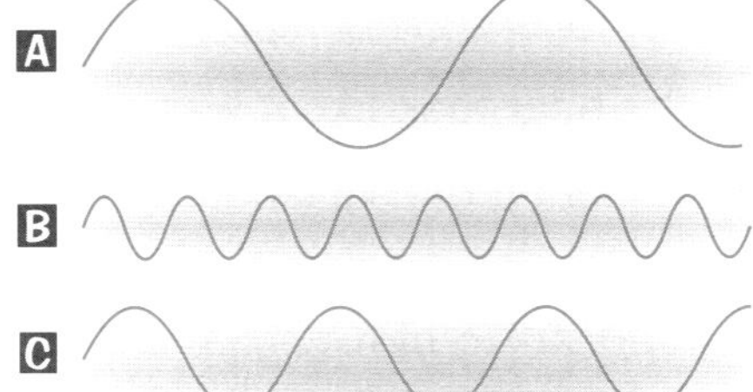


## Top Tip

You need to know that different **colours** of light have different **wavelengths** — and that you can split white light up into the colours of the rainbow. You can work out the frequency of light waves quite easily, because the **speed of light** is always the **same**.

# Sound Waves

**Q1** What has to happen for a sound wave to be created?

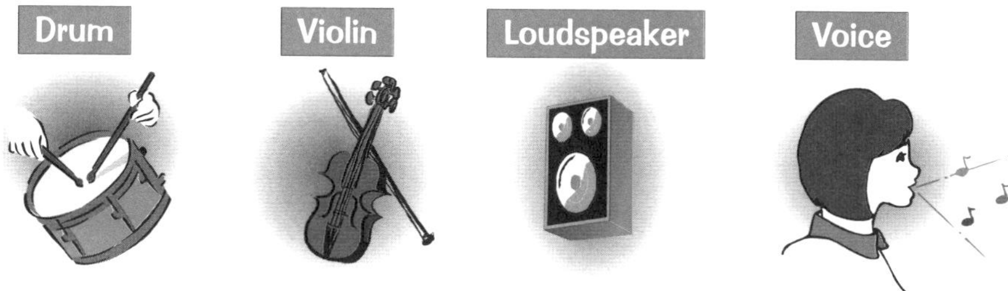


**Q2** What **vibrates** in the above objects to start a sound?

**Q3** How does the vibration travel from the object to your ear?

**Q4** **Sketch the diagram** below and complete the labelling.

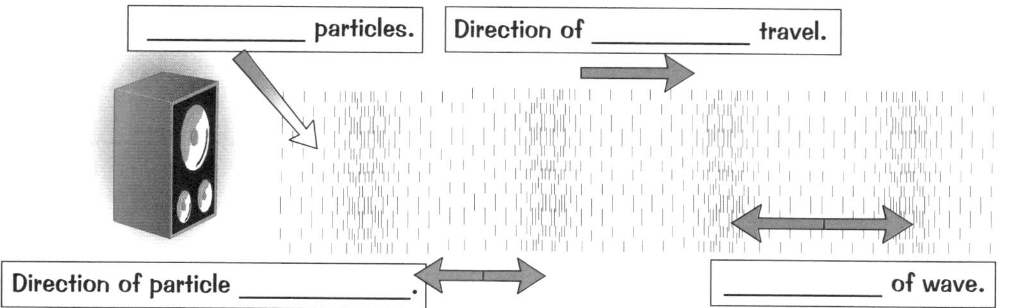


**Q5** Are sound waves **longitudinal** or **transverse**?

**Q6** How does the speed of sound compare to the speed of light? **Describe** an everyday observation which demonstrates this fact.

**Q7** *The diagram below shows a sound wave experiment. The bell is switched on and the pump started.*

a) What happens to the sound coming from the bell once the pump is started?

b) What conclusion can be drawn from this?

c) What is the purpose of the foam block?

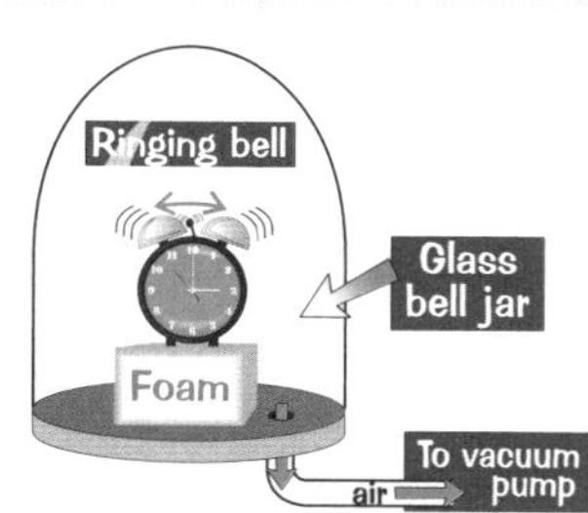


**Q8** *Six frequencies are listed below.*

**2Hz, 20Hz, 200Hz, 2000Hz, 2kHz, 20kHz**

a) Which two frequencies are **identical**?

b) Which is closest to the lowest frequency **humans** can hear?

c) For which one could you easily count the vibrations without instruments?

d) Which is closest to the **highest** frequency humans can hear?

**Q9** **Copy and complete** the statement below adding the missing words:-

As people get __________ the __________ frequency of sound that they can hear gets __________. This makes it __________ to clearly distinguish spoken words. This damage happens faster if people are regularly exposed to __________ noises.

# Sound Waves

**Q10** Complete the sentences **a)** to **c)** below:

**a)** Noise is defined as unwanted__________ and is a form of __________ in the environment.

**b)** Levels of noise are measured in _____________.

**c)** Materials which reduce noise are called sound _____________ and include carpets, curtains and _____________ glazing.

**Q11** List **five** sources of noise pollution.

**Q12** List **six** measures that can be taken to **overcome** noise problems.

Include:
- *Two measures that can be taken by* **national or local government**.
- *Two that can be taken by individuals to prevent making unwanted noise.*
- *Two that can be taken by individuals to protect themselves from excessive noise.*

**Q13** *Sound travels through some things, but not through others.*

**a)** Which of the following can sound travel through? **Mark** with a tick.

| ☐ SOLIDS | ☐ A VACUUM | ☐ LIQUIDS | ☐ GASES |
|---|---|---|---|

**b)** For each of the media you have chosen in **a)**, give *ONE piece of evidence* to show that sound can travel through that medium.

**c)** **Which** medium in **a)** does sound generally travel the fastest in?

**Q14** *If sound is a wave it must be able to do three things that all waves do.*

**a)** These are ___________, ___________ and ____________.

**b)** What is the common name for a sound reflection?

**c)** *When you are in a room with the door open, you can hear sounds coming from outside the room wherever you are standing in the room.*

Describe how this is possible.

RING
RING
RING
RING

**Q15** A spectator on a sports field is 200m from the start. She sees the starting gun fire and then hears the sound of the shot 0.6s later.

**a)** **Calculate the speed** of the sound.

**b)** What will be the **wavelength**, if the frequency of the sound is 200Hz?

**c)** Another sound wave has a frequency of 2000Hz. How does its frequency compare to the wave in part **b)**? What will the ratio of their **wavelengths** be?

**Q16** *In water a sound wave of 200Hz has a wavelength of 7m.*

How fast does it travel?

**Q17** **Calculate the wavelength** of a sound travelling in steel with a frequency of 200Hz, if the speed of sound in steel is 5000m/s.

## Top Tip

More waves, more calculations, more fun. You have to know what makes sound waves and how they travel — remember that sound won't travel in a vacuum. You won't need to know the range of human hearing by heart, but you will need to have a good idea of what frequencies we can't hear.

# Pitch and Loudness

Copy and complete, choosing words from the box opposite.

| | | |
|---|---|---|
| frequency | medium | vacuum |
| 400 | transverse | vibration |
| wavelength | wave | 330 |
| longitudinal | amplitude | |

**Q1** Sound is a type of ____________ motion.

**Q2** To make a sound wave there must be a ____________ .

**Q3** Sound is a ____________ wave.

**Q4** Sound waves travel at about ____________ m/s in air.

**Q5** The distance between successive compressions of the wave is the ____________ .

**Q6** The number of vibrations per second is called the ____________ .

**Q7** The maximum distance of particles from their resting position is called the ____________ of the wave.

**Q8** Sound cannot travel through a ____________, but needs a ____________ to travel in.

**Q9** *A tuning fork is struck producing a high pitched sound.*

**a)** Explain **how** the sound is produced.

**b)** Describe a way of measuring the frequency of the tuning fork.

**c)** What difference would you hear if a tuning fork with longer prongs is struck?

**d)** How could you visually show there is vibration without the aid of an oscilloscope?

**Q10** *An oscilloscope visually displays electrical signals.*

**a)** **What can be used** to convert sound into an electrical signal, needed by the oscilloscope?

**b)** A tuning fork produces a single pure note. **Sketch** the shape of the wave you would expect to see on an oscilloscope trace.

**Q11** *Sarah is experimenting with an oscilloscope and a signal generator connected to a loudspeaker.*

*She draws an oscilloscope trace for a range of frequencies and amplitudes (see opposite) but gets the labels mixed up.*

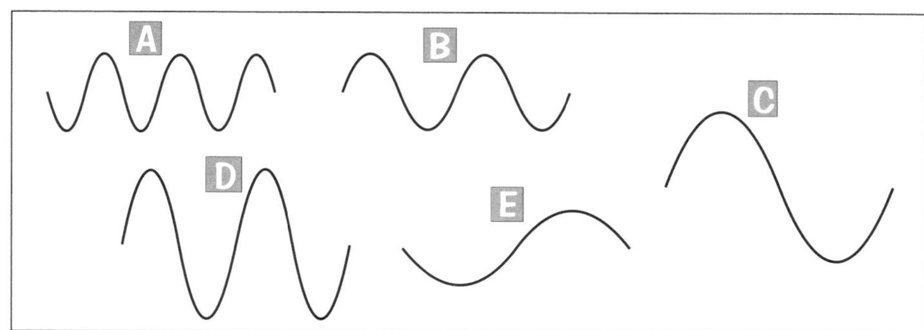


**a)** Study the traces above and complete the missing data in the table opposite.

**b)** What is the difference in the sound of the traces B and D.

| Oscilloscope Trace | Frequency (Hz) | Amplitude (V) |
|---|---|---|
| | 100 | 2 |
| | 100 | 4 |
| | 200 | 2 |
| | 200 | 4 |
| | 300 | 2 |

# Pitch and Loudness

**Q12** *Changing the frequency or amplitude of a sound wave affects the type of sound you hear.*

**Choose the correct words** to complete the paragraph below:-

> **"Increasing the [frequency / amplitude] of a sound will [raise/lower] the pitch of the sound, producing a [higher / lower] note. Decreasing the [frequency / amplitude] will [raise/lower] the pitch of the sound. Increasing the amplitude will increase the [pitch / loudness] of the sound and decreasing the amplitude will make the sound [louder / quieter / higher / lower]."**

**Q13** *Kerry is using the equipment shown below to investigate high frequency sounds.*

She records:

- *the frequency*
- *the amplitude*
- *what she hears*
- *a drawing of the oscilloscope picture*

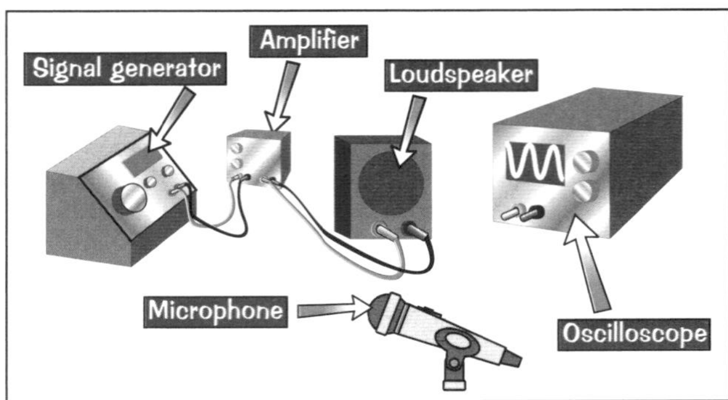


She recorded the results in a table like the one below. The first line of her table is filled in.

| Drawing | Frequency (Hz) | Amplitude (V) | Sound heard |
|---|---|---|---|
| | 10 000 | 2V | High and Quiet |
| | 15 000 | 4V | |
| | 20 000 | 2V | |
| | 25 000 | 2V | |

a) **Complete** the table with the results you would expect her to find for the other frequencies.

b) **Why is it difficult** to be certain about the last column for 20 000Hz?

c) What animal might hear the highest frequency in the table?

## Top Tip

It's **mega-important** to understand an oscilloscope picture — questions about oscilloscope pictures are **very popular** in exams. Remember that a **taller** trace means a **higher amplitude** which means a **louder sound**. Remember that more ups and downs means a **higher frequency** which means a **higher pitch**.

# Ultrasound

Ultrasound is sound with a higher frequency than we can hear.

**Q1** *A signal generator can be used with a loudspeaker and amplifier to make sounds of a large frequency range (see below). An oscilloscope displays the sounds as traces.*

**a)** What **kind of signal** is produced by a signal generator?

**b)** What does the **loudspeaker** do to this signal?

**c)** What can the oscilloscope be used for in this set up?

**d)** Why does the oscilloscope need a microphone attached to it?

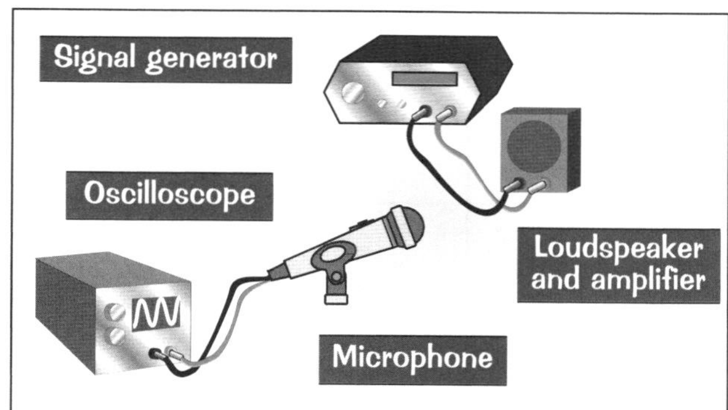


**Q2** *An oscilloscope is set to give a clear signal at 10 kHz.*

**a)** What change would you see on the oscilloscope if the frequency is changed to **20kHz**.

**b)** What change would you **hear**?

**c)** If the frequency is increased to 25kHz what changes would you see and hear?

**Q3** Copy and complete the following:

"Sounds above 20 000Hz have too high a ____________ to be heard by the human ear. Such sounds can be converted from ______________ oscillations using a loudspeaker. Sounds above this frequency are called ______________."

**Q4** Calculate the wavelengths of the following ultrasound frequencies *(in air)*.
— *Take the speed of sound in air to be 330m/s.*

| **a)** 25kHz | **b)** 30kHz | **c)** 50kHz | **d)** 100kHz |
|---|---|---|---|

**Q5** Why is it important to state that the sounds are travelling through air?

**Q6** **What frequency** will a sound wave have in air if its wavelength is 0.5cm?

**Q7** *Bats use ultrasound to catch their prey. A typical victim would be a mosquito or a small moth.*

*A bat can not sense anything smaller than the wavelength of sound it uses.*

**What frequency** does the bat need to send out, to help catch a mosquito?

Hint *(you first have to estimate the size of a mosquito...)*

# Ultrasound

**Q8** *You should be able to describe several applications that humans have found for ultrasound.*

Below is a table summarising six uses of ultrasound. The information is all mixed up.

| Application | Category of use | Ultrasound used to | Basic principles |
|---|---|---|---|
| Removal of kidney stones | Industrial | Image the foetus | Use of energy in ultrasound to physically alter material |
| Quality control | Medical | Shatter stones allowing them to be passed out in urine | Use of energy in ultrasound to physically alter material |
| Removal of tartar | Military / Scientific | Break up tartar deposits on teeth | Use of energy in ultrasound to physically alter material |
| Sonar | Medical | Check for cracks in metal castings | Detection of reflected ultrasound to build image |
| Pre-natal screening | Industrial | Cleaning delicate mechanisms without dismantling them | Detection of reflected ultrasound to build image |
| Cleaning | Medical | Measure distances to objects or map the sea bed | Detection of reflected ultrasound to build image |

**Redraw** the table with the information in the **correct places**.

**Q9** **Copy and complete**:-

"Ultrasound is useful for imaging because it is partially ____________ at the boundaries of different ____________. The reflection can be processed to form an ____________ of the internal ____________ of the object under study."

**Q10** Why is ultrasound...

**a)** better than X-rays for looking at a foetus?

**b)** better for cleaning delicate mechanisms than traditional methods?

**c)** better for treating kidney stones than open surgery?

**d)** the chosen method for checking for flaws in metal castings?

**e)** used to remove tartar?

**Q11** There are other practical uses of ultrasound.

**a)** Submarines use it to calculate the distance to objects. How?

**b)** What is this process called?

**c)** There are less obvious uses for ultrasound such as in autofocus cameras.
How do you think it is used in this case?

## Top Tip

Well, it's pretty obvious what ultrasound is. In the syllabus, they expect you to be able to name **four** examples of where **ultrasound** is used, and to say what the **benefits** are of using ultrasound rather than some other mechanism. There's more practice with the standard wave equation on these pages, too.

# The Speed of Sound

**Q1** What is the speed of sound in **air** in metres per second?

**Q2** What is the name for a **reflected** sound?

**Q3** How is the speed of sound different in **water** compared to **air**? It's quicker in water, because there's small distance between particles in water then in air.

**Q4** *A group of students has been sent outside to estimate the speed of sound. One student bangs two wooden blocks together. Two other students measure the time between the bang and hearing the reflected sound from a large wall. They measure the time interval several times. The distance to the wall is 200m.*

Their ten different recorded times are shown in the table below.

| Time Interval (s) | | | | |
|---|---|---|---|---|
| 1.11 | 1.23 | 1.29 | 1.17 | 1.15 |
| 1.19 | 1.21 | 1.13 | 1.27 | 1.25 |

a) Calculate the **average** of these times. 1.2s

b) **How far** did the sound actually travel during this time? 1.2s

c) What is the **speed of sound** deduced from this experiment?

d) Why is it a good idea to repeat the experiment?

e) If they had calculated the speed of sound using **only one** of their measured times, what is the maximum error that could have occurred in their calculation?

**Q5** *Some other students try a different way of measuring the speed of sound.*

*The students are positioned at 200m intervals across the field. Each has a stopwatch. The student with the starting pistol simultaneously pulls the trigger and drops his arm. The students start their stop watches when they see the arm fall, and stop the watches when they hear the bang.*

Their times are summarised in the table below.

| Distance (m) | 200 | 400 | 600 | 800 | 1 000 |
|---|---|---|---|---|---|
| Time (s) | 0.9 | 1.2 | 1.8 | 2.4 | 3.0 |

a) **Plot a graph** of distance from the pistol against time.

b) Use your graph to calculate the speed of sound.

c) One point does not quite fit the pattern. Why might you expect this point to be the one **least accurately** measured?

# The Speed of Sound

**Q6** *A small submarine is using sonar to locate objects in murky water.*

*There are several objects in it's projected path.*
*These objects are: a large submarine; a whale; a shipwreck; the seabed.*
*The submarine sends a pulse out in front and receives four echoes.*
*It moves forward 75m and sends another pulse, again receiving four echoes.*

The table below shows the time taken for the first and second echoes to be received from each of the 4 objects.

| Object | Time for First Echo (s) | Time for Second Echo (s) |
|---|---|---|
| 1 | 0.2 | 0.1 |
| 2 | 0.1 | 0.1 |
| 3 | 0.4 | 0.2 |
| 4 | 1.0 | 1.1 |

The speed of sound in water is 1500m/s.

**a)** What distance away is each object at the time of the first echo?

**b)** What distance away is each object at the time of the second echo?

**c)** Remembering that the small submarine has moved between receiving the first and second echoes: **What can you say** about the movement of the other objects?

**d)** **Identify** the seabed and the shipwreck.

**e)** Now choose which of the objects left is the whale and which is the submarine? It will be helpful to note that submarines are more inquisitive than whales.

Sound is a wave and there are two equations for calculating the speed of a wave.

**Q7** *A sophisticated method of measuring sound involves the use of a metal bar and an oscilloscope.*
*A sound with a frequency of 10 kHz takes 0.0004s to travel along a 1m steel bar and return.*

**a)** How far has the sound wave travelled?

**b)** What equation would you use to **calculate the wave's speed**?

**c)** What is its speed? Is this faster or slower than speed in air?

**d)** What equation would you use to calculate the wavelength?

**e)** What **is** its wavelength?

## Top Tip

It's simple — **speed = distance/time**. The **really important** thing to remember when doing the **echo questions** is that the sound has to travel **to** the wall **and back**, so it's travelled **double** the distance. Light travels so fast that you can just assume that you see something at the exact moment that it happens.

# Reflection

**Q1** *Like sound, light can be reflected off surfaces. Complete the gaps in the sentences below.*

**a)** Some objects give out their own light. All other objects we see because they ______________ light.

**b)** Some objects reflect light without sending it off in many different directions. This is called a ____________ reflection and objects which do this look ____________.

**c)** Most objects send the reflected light in many different directions, giving a ____________ reflection. These objects look ____________.

**d)** The law of reflection states that "the angle of ______________ is ______________ to the angle of ______________."

**Q2** What is the name for a beam of light used to represent a light path?

**Q3** What is the name for the line drawn at right angles to a mirror surface?

**Q4** The diagrams 1, 2 and 3 shows rays arriving at a surface.

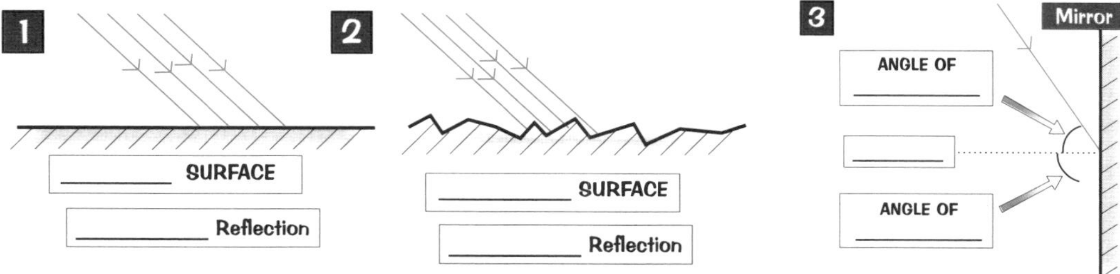


Make a copy of each diagram. Complete the labels and draw the reflected rays.

**Q5** Study this plan view of two people sitting on a park bench.

They can see some statues reflected in the window.

Use the law of reflection to decide **which of the statues**, A, B, C, and D, persons 1 and 2 can see?

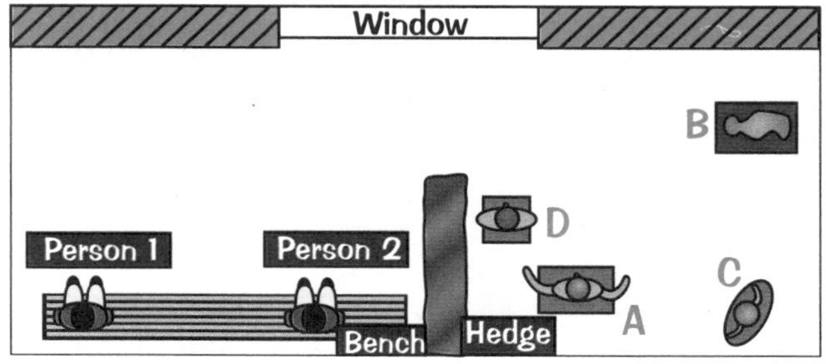


**Q6** In the diagram opposite, rays are falling on the curved mirrors 1 and 2.

**a)** Draw the diagrams and complete the ray paths for the reflections.

**b)** Name the shapes of the two mirrors.

**c)** List two uses for each of the mirrors 1 and 2.

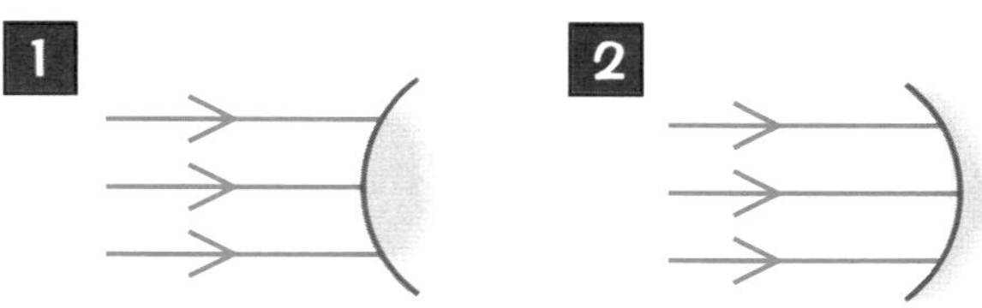


## Top Tips

You've got to learn the **diagrams** in question 4 and be able to **draw** them, so practise. Also, you need to be able to draw a diagram to show how an image is formed in a flat mirror. Watch out with your labels — the angles of incidence and reflection are between the ray and the **normal**, **not** the ray and the **surface**.

# Refraction

**Q1** **Fill in the gaps or choose the correct words** *for the following sentences about refraction.*

**a)** Light travels at different __________ in different media.

**b)** Light will [speed up/ slow down] when it travels from air into glass.

**c)** When the light goes back into air it will [speed up/ slow down].

**d)** The change of speed occurs at the ______________ of the two media.

**Q2** What is meant by the "**normal**" to a surface?

**Q3** Does the **frequency** of light change as it enters a different medium?

**Q4** *Study the rays in the two diagrams on the right.*

**a)** In Diagram 1, a ray **enters** a glass block. Which ray X, Y or Z, shows how it would continue?

**b)** In Diagram 2, a ray **leaves** the block. Which ray A, B or C shows its path correctly?

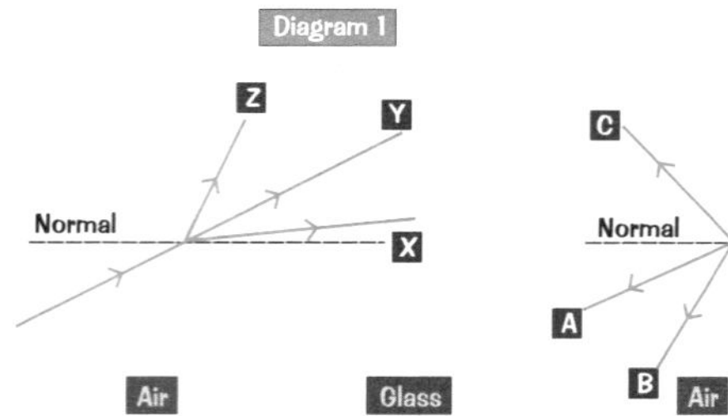


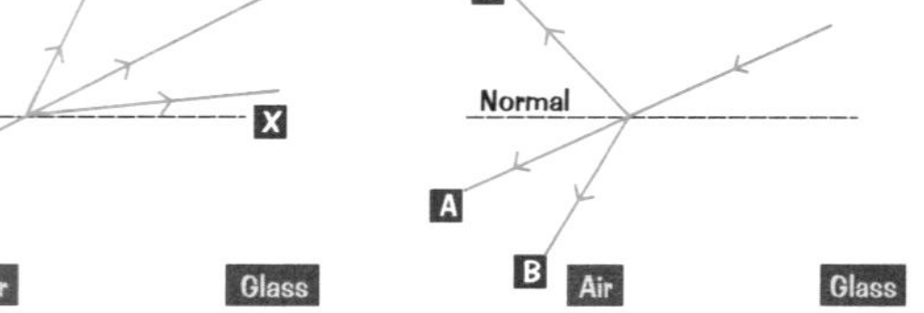


**Q5** **Copy and complete**:

> **When a ray of light enters a glass block it is bent [towards / away from] the normal.**
> **When a ray of light leaves the glass block it is bent [towards / away from] the normal.**

**Q6** *This diagram shows a ray of light entering a glass block as a* **wavefront**.

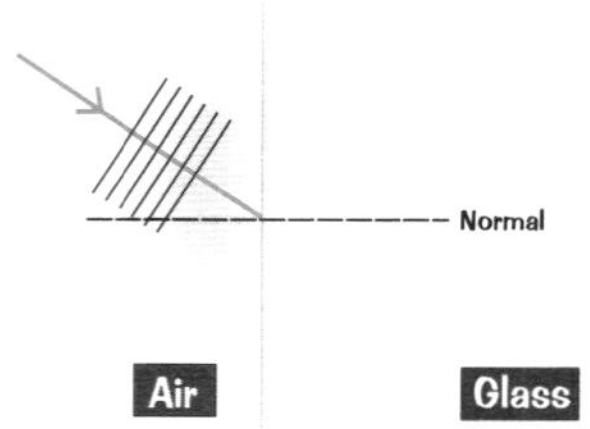


**Write an explanation** of the refraction of this ray in the block using the idea of a wavefront — use the **key words** opposite to help you.

**KEYWORDS**
angle to normal
- wavefront
- slows down
- wavelength
- direction changed
- frequency is unchanged

**Q7** *The diagram below shows the ray of light leaving a glass block as a wavefront.*

**KEYWORDS**
angle to normal
- wavefront
- speeds up
- wavelength
- direction changed
- frequency is unchanged

**Write an explanation** of the refraction of this ray as it exits the block, using the idea of a wavefront — use the **key words** opposite to help you.

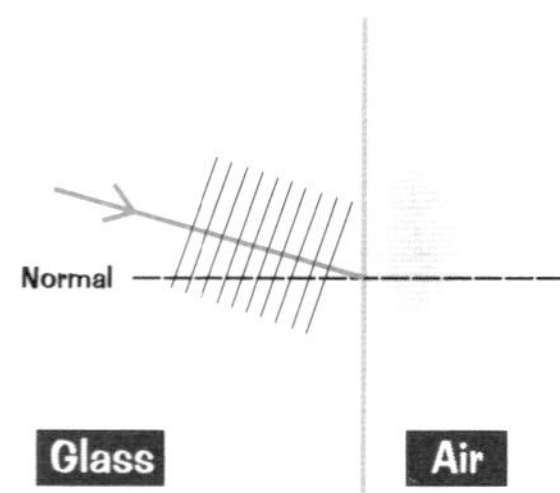


## Top Tips

**Refraction** and **Reflection** — the words look similar, but they're not the same. You need to know **what** refraction is and **how it happens**. Learn all the diagrams, they can ask you to draw them in the Exam. Remember that the light **won't** be bent if it enters at **exactly 90°**, but it **still slows down**.

# Special Cases of Refraction

**Q1** Make a copy of the prism opposite, with a monochromatic light ray entering it as shown.

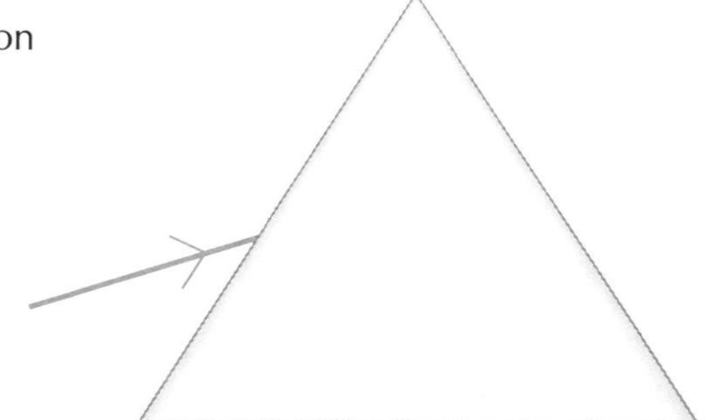

**a)** Draw the normal to the face where the ray enters.

**b)** How will the wavelength and speed of the ray change on entering the prism?

**c)** Draw the ray path to the other side of the prism.

**d)** Draw the normal to the face where the ray leaves the prism.

**e)** Draw the ray outside the prism.

**f)** If the ray of light was "white" light from sunlight, what else would you see happen?

**Q2** List as many instruments you can think of that use prisms.

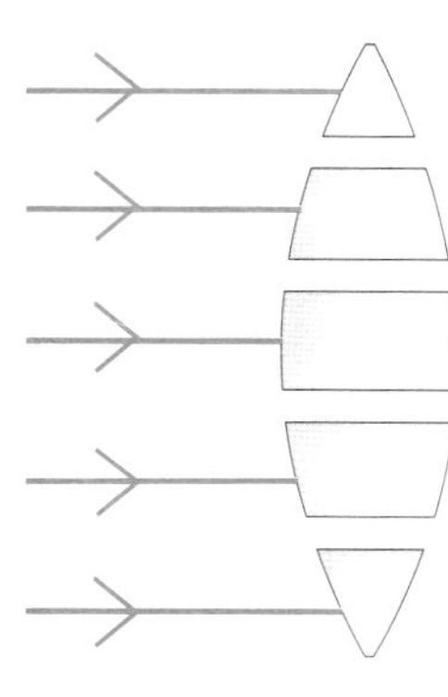

**Q3** *A lens can be thought of as lots of separate prisms acting together. The lens on the left is split into five prisms.*

**a)** What type of lens is pictured in the diagram opposite.

**b)** Draw normals to the rays entering the top three prisms.

**c)** Complete the ray paths in the glass and leaving the glass.

**d)** Complete the bottom two prisms by comparing them to your answer to part **c)**.

**e)** Describe the purpose of a lens this shape.

**Q4** Copy and complete this paragraph about total internal reflection.

> **"Total internal reflection happens when light is travelling in a material like [glass / air] and comes to the [edge / middle] of the block. If the light meets the boundary at a large angle to the [edge / normal], the ray is [refracted / diffracted / reflected], not [refracted / reflected]. The angle at which internal reflection begins is called the [critical / incident / normal] angle and is about [22 / 42 / 90] degrees in glass"**

**Q5** Make a copy of the glass block below, with a light ray entering it as shown.

**a)** Draw the normal to the block at the point where the ray enters.

**b)** How will the direction of the ray change on entering? Why is this?

**c)** Continue the ray inside the block.

**X**

**d)** Draw in the normal to the face where the ray will leave the block. Draw the ray leaving the block.

**e)** *If the ray had come in through point X originally, the result would have been quite different.* Draw a ray coming in through point X directed towards o. Show its path through the glass and then exiting the block. What is the effect called that occurs on the flat side of the block?

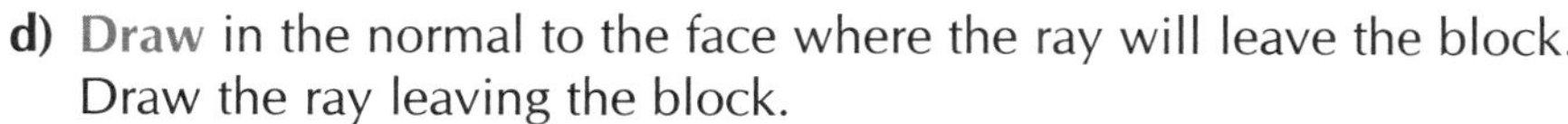

# Total Internal Reflection

**Q1** *The diagram shows two identical glass blocks with a ray entering at two different angles.*

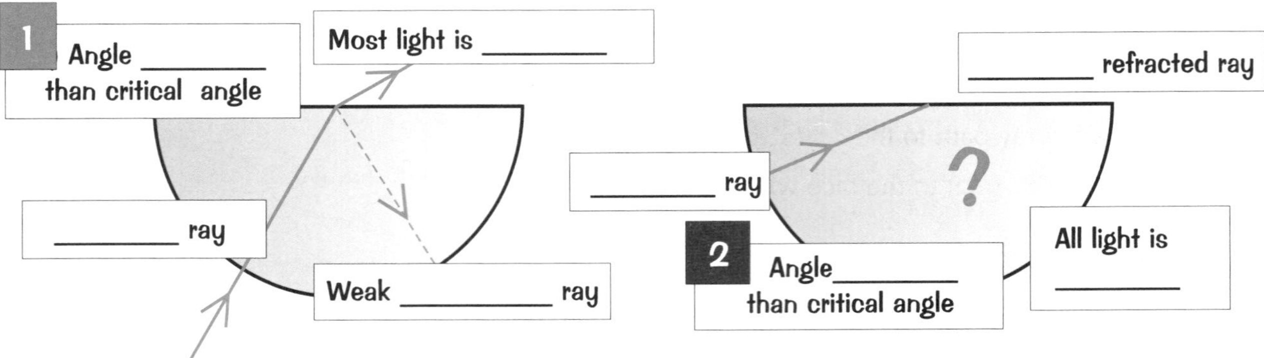


a) **Copy** Diagram 1 and **complete** the labelling.

b) **Copy** Diagram 2. **Draw** the reflected ray inside the block and **complete** the labelling.

**Q2** *The diagram below shows a ray of light entering a glass prism at right-angles to a surface.*

a) Why does the ray enter the prism without changing direction?

b) Copy the diagram opposite. Mark the angle of incidence and the angle of reflection, and label them.

c) What is the value of the angle of incidence at the inside surface?

d) What must be true about the angle of incidence and the angle of reflection?

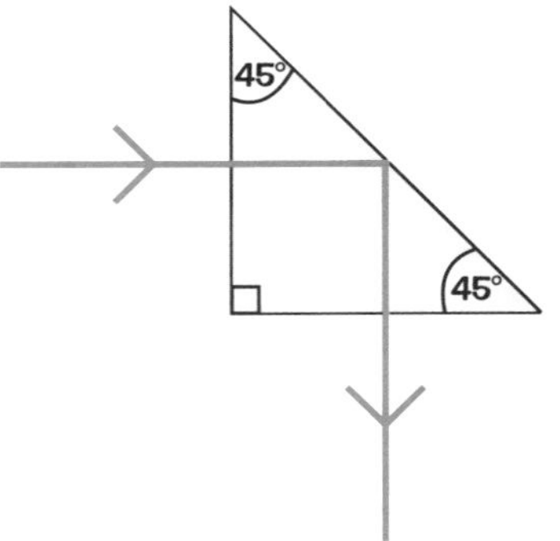


**Q3** a) **Draw a diagram** of an optical fibre, showing:

- **the layers of the fibre**
- **the light ray travelling along it (show 3 or 4 reflections)**

Mark with arrows where total internal reflection occurs.

b) State the **advantages** of optical fibres over wires for carrying information.

**Q4** **Describe** what an endoscope is, and give a use of an endoscope in a hospital. Can you think of one other use of total internal reflection?

## Top Tip

**Prisms** and **lenses** use refraction. You need to know **which way** the colours go in the rainbow from a prism — think about which colour is refracted **most** and which is refracted **least**. Remember that Total Internal Reflection is a special example of light 'refracting' between a dense material and air.

# Diffraction

**Q1** **Fill in the gaps** in the following sentences...

**a)** Waves will ____________ when they go through a ______________ or past an ____________.

**b)** This effect is called ______________.

**c)** The ______________ the gap the more diffraction there is.

**d)** If the gap is about the same size as the ______________ of the wave, a _____ __________ shaped wave will be produced.

**Q2** *"Sound diffracts more than light."*

**Describe** what this statement means and explain why sound behaves differently.

**Q3** *The following diagrams show plane waves approaching an obstacle.*

**a)**

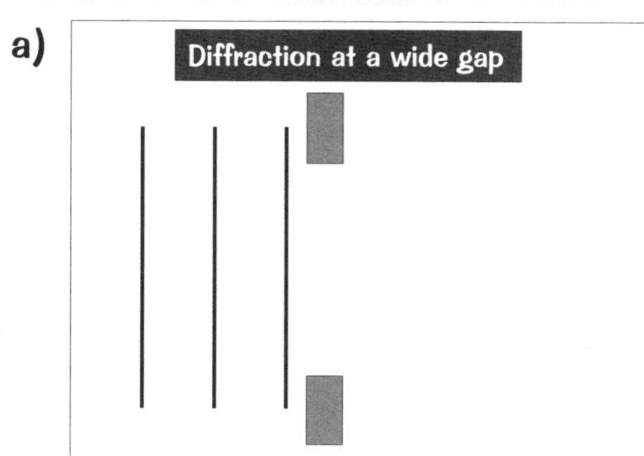


**b)**

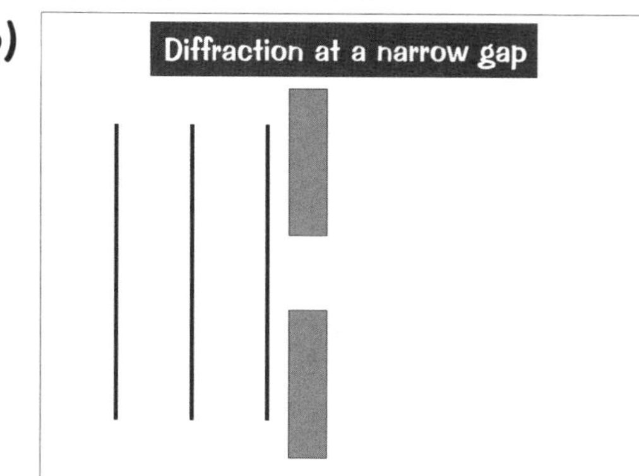


**c)**

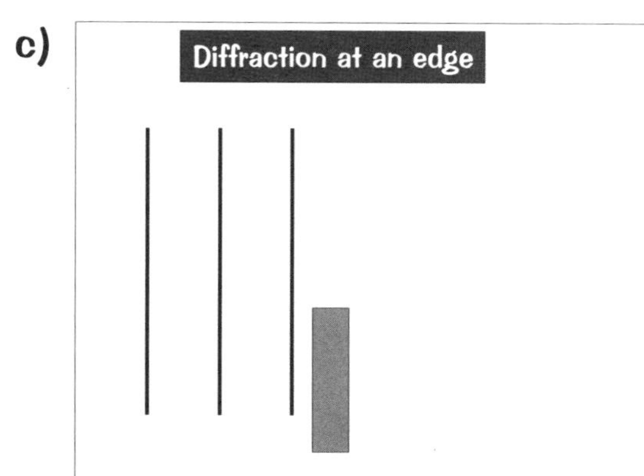


**d)**

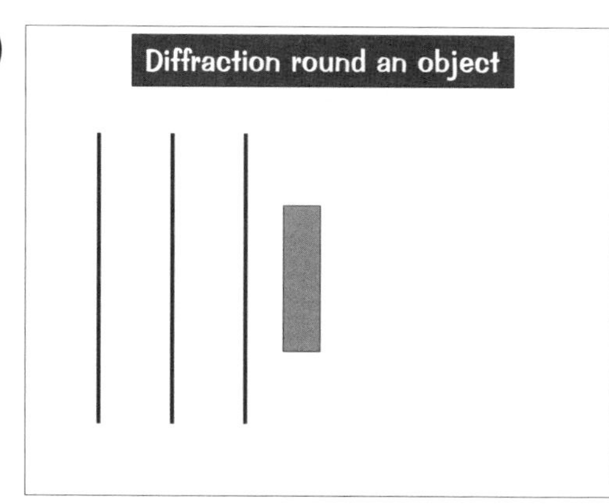


Copy the diagrams and draw the wavefronts after passing the obstacles.

***(Speed of sound = 330m/s, speed of light = 3 x $10^8$ m/s)***

**Q4** *A sound wave and visible light wave pass through a doorway 75cm wide.*

**a)** What **frequency of sound** has a wavelength of 75cm? Can a human **hear** this sound?

**b)** If the visible light wave has a frequency of 5 x $10^{14}$ Hz, what is its wavelength?

**c)** Use the results of your calculations **a)** and **b)** to **explain** why it is possible to hear around corners, but not possible to see around corners.

**Q5** **What frequency** of electromagnetic radiation has a wavelength of 75cm? What type EM radiation is this?

# Diffraction

**Q6** *This diagram shows an experiment to demonstrate the diffraction of light.*

The laser shines red light through a narrow slit. The light shows up on a white screen.

Laser
Red Light
Screen
Narrow slit

**a)** Why is laser light used instead of an ordinary light source?

**b)** How is the beam path made visible?

**c)** Why does the slit have to be **very narrow**?

**d)** One student looks at the screen and says, "That's just an image of the slit!" How could you show that he was wrong?

**e)** How would the shape of the beam change if the slit was replaced with a **narrower** one?

**f)** How would the shape of the beam change if **green light** was used **instead** of red light?

**Q7** How can you predict whether a radiowave will show significant diffraction around an obstacle?

**Q8** Will significant diffraction occur for the following situations, and what will be the effect?

**a)** A long wave radio signal of frequency 1MHz passes between 2 blocks of flats 250m apart.

**b)** An FM radio signal of frequency 1GHz is transmitted from the far side of a short tunnel that is 6m wide.

**c)** I am sitting at my desk and outside my window (50cm wide) irate drivers are blowing their horns (frequency 5000Hz).

**Q9** The diagrams below show shortwave TV waves and longwave radiowaves approaching a hill.

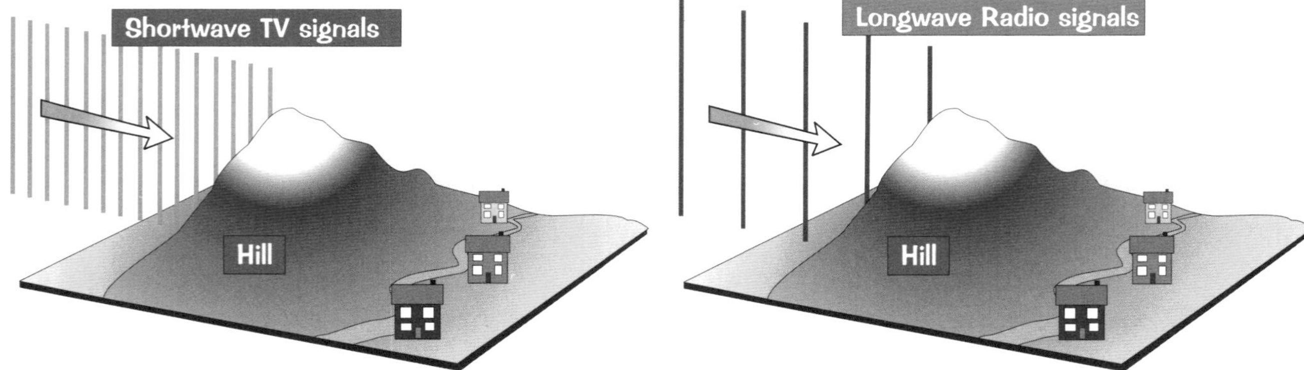


**a)** Copy and complete the pictures above, showing how the hill changes the direction of the EM wave.

**b)** Suggest a reason why people in the houses in the picture could listen to the cricket match on Test Match Special on longwave Radio 4 but not be able to watch it on the television.

## Top Tip

Diffraction just means the **spreading out** of waves. The thing to remember here is that waves spread out **more** going through a **narrow** gap than a **wide** gap — a narrow gap is one about the **same size** as the **wavelength**. Once again, there's diagrams to be copied and learnt — look at question 3.

# Optical Instruments

*Optical instruments all rely upon basic principles which you should know inside out.*

**Q1** **Copy and complete** the following sentences.

"When a ray of light moves from air into glass it bends [ away from / towards ] the normal.
When a ray of light moves from glass into air it bends [ away from / towards ] the normal."

**Q2** *Lenses work by refracting light.*

The two lenses opposite have light rays approaching them from infinity.

Copy the diagrams and show how the light rays would be refracted by the lenses.

a) 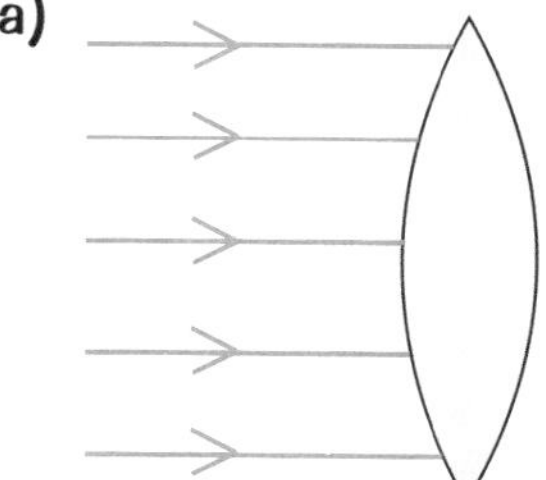

b) 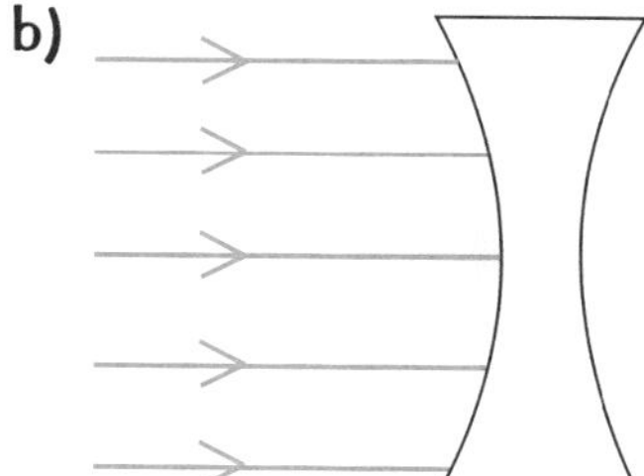

**Q3** *The diagram below shows a Single Lens Reflex (SLR) camera, popular with photographers.*
Which part of the camera...

a) controls the amount of light entering the camera?
b) focuses the light?
c) records the image?
d) allows the light in when the photograph is taken?

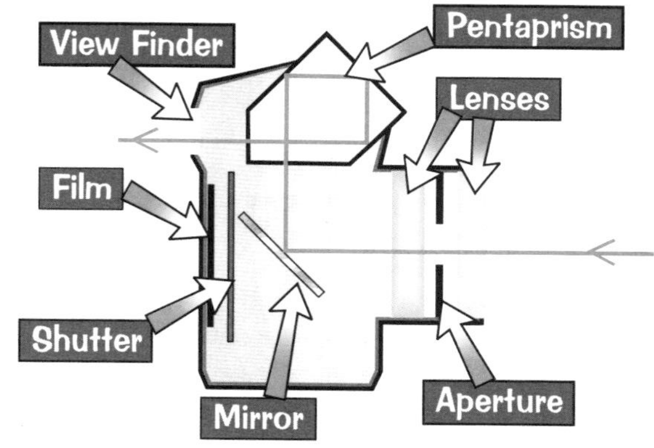


**Q4** *In an SLR camera, another part has to move to allow a photograph to be taken.*

a) Which part is this?
b) Why is this part "in the way" the rest of the time?

**Q5** What **type of reflection** is occurring inside the pentaprism?

**Q6** What advantages are there in using this complicated arrangement with a pentaprism?

The diagram opposite shows a standard pair of binoculars.

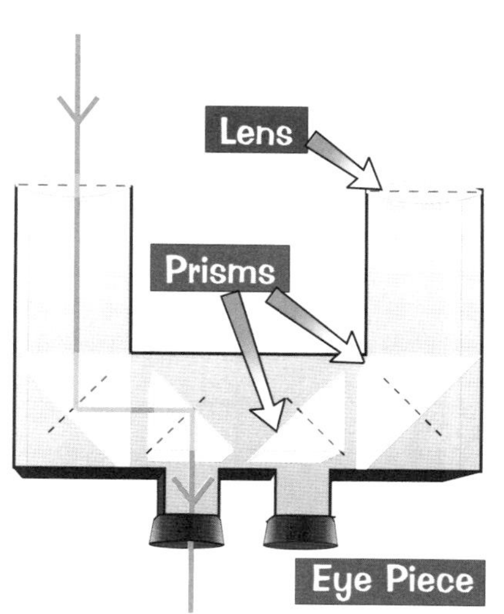


**Q7** *The lens and eyepiece are offset, so that prisms are needed to bend the light through the binoculars.*
What is the reason for this complicated arrangement?

**Q8** **Complete** the light path for the other half of the binoculars.

**Q9** *Mirrors can be used instead of prisms.*
Describe one advantage of using highly reflective mirrors rather than prisms.

**Q10** What property of the prism allows light to be 'bent' around corners?

# Optical Instruments

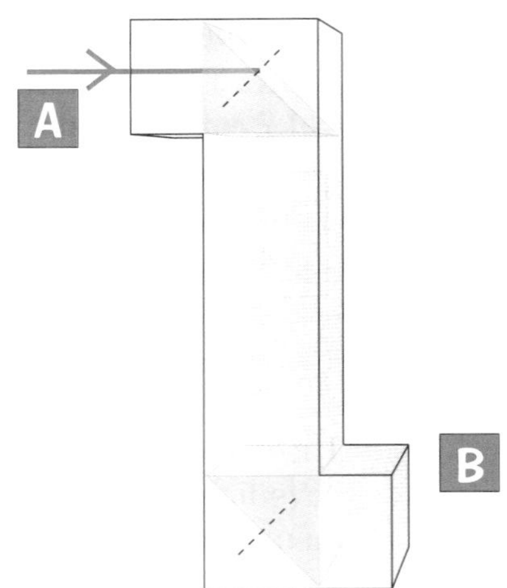


**Q11** *The diagram opposite shows light entering a periscope.*

a) Copy the diagram and **draw the light path** through the periscope.

b) How does the positioning of the prisms ensure there is no **dispersion** of the light rays when they pass through the periscope?

c) Where on the periscope would you put your eye to view a scene from a higher point?

d) What is the advantage (when looking through the periscope) of lengthening the column A-B?

**Q12** a) Give two uses for a periscope.

b) Explain why the periscope is needed in each case.

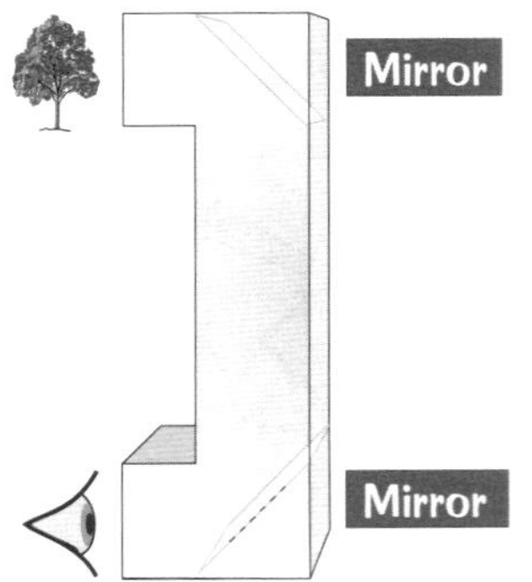


**Q13** *This diagram shows a mirror periscope that has been put together* incorrectly.

a) Copy the diagram and draw the paths of two light rays travelling to the eye — one from the **top of the tree** and one from **the trunk**.

b) What **problem** can you identify with this periscope?

c) This time, **draw the periscope correctly**, with two new light rays showing how this version works as it should do.

d) List two **advantages** of using mirrors in a periscope rather than prisms.

**Q14** *The diagram below shows a light ray being reflected by a bicycle* **reflector**.

a) Explain how the incident ray is **reflected back** in the direction it came from.

This reflector will reflect light coming in from other angles too.

b) What would you expect to happen to the light ray at 'E'? (Will it be reflected back the way it came or will it leave at a different angle?)

c) What will happen to the light ray 'F'?

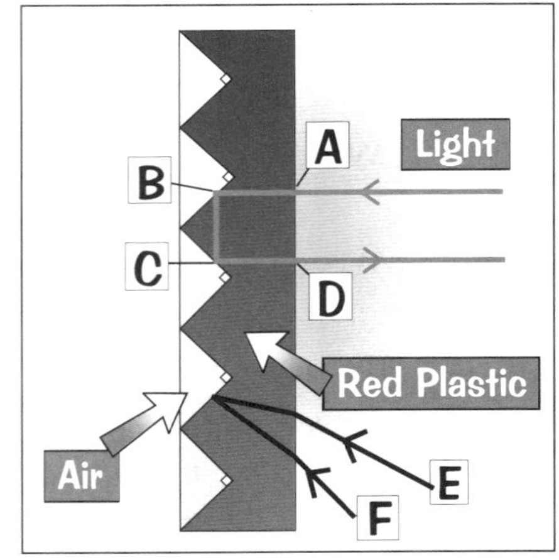


**Q15** What do the **shapes** of the prisms in a **reflector**, in **binoculars** and in a **periscope** have in common?

## Top Tip

These are all smashing examples of reflection, refraction and total internal reflection. **Learn** the diagrams and **practise** drawing them, because they could ask you to fill in a partly drawn diagram of one of these instruments in the Exam. They're not difficult, but there are quite a few little details to remember.

# The Electromagnetic Spectrum

**Q1** *Copy and complete the following paragraphs about electromagnetic waves.*

a) Electromagnetic (EM) waves form a continuous___________. For a given _________ all EM waves travel with roughly the same _____________. In a ___________ this___________ is about 3 x $10^8$ m/s. There are ____________ main types of EM wave. The correct order for these types of EM wave is (beginning with longest wavelength):

______ _____, _____________, ______ _______, ______ _______, _______ _______, ___________ and _______ _______.

b) ____________ waves have the lowest frequency and the _________ wavelength, and _________ ________ have the highest frequency and the ____________ wavelength. Our eyes are sensitive to EM waves from the ______________ spectrum only.

**Q2** *For each of the statements* **a)** *to* **j)** *below, state whether it is* **true or false**, *and* **if it is false**, *write down what the* **underlined words** *should be replaced with.*

a) **Microwaves** are used to communicate with satellites.

b) **Microwaves** are the same thing as heat radiation.

c) **Gamma rays** both cause and cure cancer.

d) Only **visible light** will show diffraction.

e) **Radio waves** can have wavelengths of many metres.

f) **X-rays** are used to take pictures of bones because they are relatively safe.

g) **Infrared** radiation causes skin cancer.

h) **Microwaves** are absorbed by water.

i) **Long wave radiowaves** are able to diffract long distances round the Earth.

j) **Visible light** has a wavelength of about a ten thousandth of a millimetre.

**Q3** *The diagram shows parts of the electromagnetic spectrum and wavelengths for the different radiations. However, they are all mixed up.*

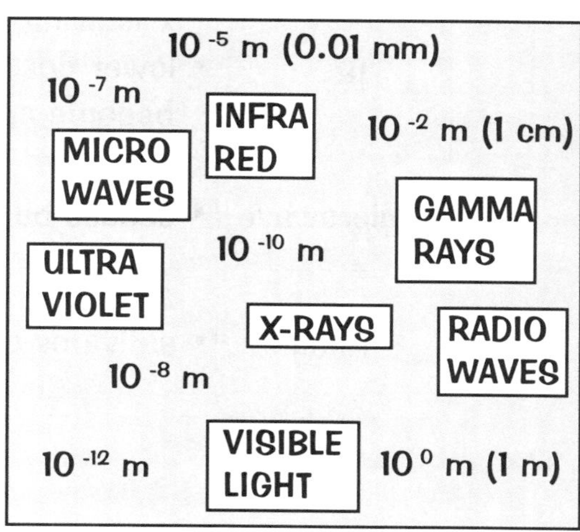


a) **Draw** your own diagram of a spectrum, but with the types of radiation and wavelengths in the correct order, from the shortest to the longest wavelength.

b) What is the **speed** of an electromagnetic wave in a vacuum?

c) Calculate the **frequency** for each type of wave.

d) How many times longer is a typical visible light wave compared with an X-ray wave?

e) How many times longer is a microwave compared with a typical visible light wave?

# The Electromagnetic Spectrum

**Q4** An electromagnetic wave is drawn on an A4 piece of paper so that one wavelength fills the page and you are told it is drawn actual size. What two types of EM wave could the drawing represent?

**Q5** A commonly used microwave wavelength is 3cm. What is its frequency?

**Q6** *This table is all mixed up!* Redraw the table with the information in the correct places.

| Type of Radiation | Effects on Living Tissue | Uses |
|---|---|---|
| Gamma | • probably none | • communication<br>• broadcasting<br>• radar |
| X-Ray | • heating of water in tissues can cause "burning" | • imaging internal structures in the body<br>• studying the atomic structure of materials |
| UV | • kills living cells in high doses<br>• lower doses can cause cells to become cancerous<br>• causes tanning | • fluorescent tubes<br>• tanning<br>• security marking |
| Visible | • kills living cells in high doses<br>• lower doses can cause cells to become cancerous<br>• kills cancerous cells | • kill bacteria in food<br>• sterilise medical equipment<br>• treat tumours |
| IR | • kills living cells in high doses<br>• lower doses can cause cells to become cancerous | • radiant heaters<br>• grills<br>• remote controls<br>• thermal imaging |
| Microwave | • causes burning of tissues | • satellite communication<br>• cooking |
| Radio | • activates sensitive cells in the retina | • seeing<br>• optical fibre communication |

## Top Tip

Lots of juicy facts. It's all important so don't skip bits. To help you learn the order of the EM spectrum you could use this phrase or perhaps invent a better one. Rabid Monkeys In Violet Underpants eXterminate Gibbons. Remember that the speed of all EM waves in a vacuum is the same, it's important.

# Seismic Waves

Do you know the facts about seismic waves?

**Q1** Seismic waves are caused by ________________.

**Q2** Seismic waves start in the Earth's ______________ from a point called the **focus**.

**Q3** The point above this on the _________________ is called the **epicentre**.

**Q4** Seismic waves are detected using a _________________.

**Q5** There are two types of seismic wave called ____________ waves and ___________ waves.

**Q6** The ____________ waves are faster. They can travel through _____________ and ______________.

**Q7** The ______________ waves are slower; they can only travel through _____________.

**Q8** _________ waves are **longitudinal**, whereas __________ waves are **transverse**.

**Q9** From studying seismic waves we have learned that the Earth contains ______ layers called (from the surface inwards); the ______________, the _____________, the __________ __________ and the ___________ __________.

**Q10** Both types of wave change direction inside the Earth due to the effect of ____________.

**Q11** The waves travel in ______________ paths. This is because of changes in the __________ of material inside the Earth.

**Q12** *The diagram shows the model we have developed for the Earth using information from seismic waves.*

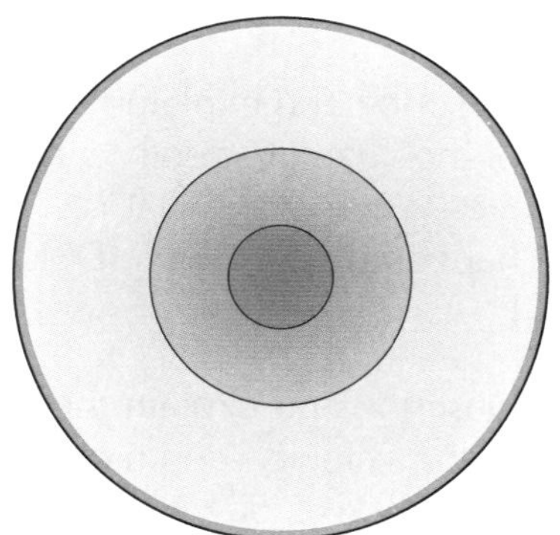

**a)** **Copy** the diagram and label the different layers that make up the Earth.

**b)** The measurement of seismic waves can be used to learn about the interior of the Earth. Why is this a more convenient method than drilling into the earth to take measurements?

Study the diagram of the Earth on the right. It shows an earthquake sending four S–Waves into the Earth.

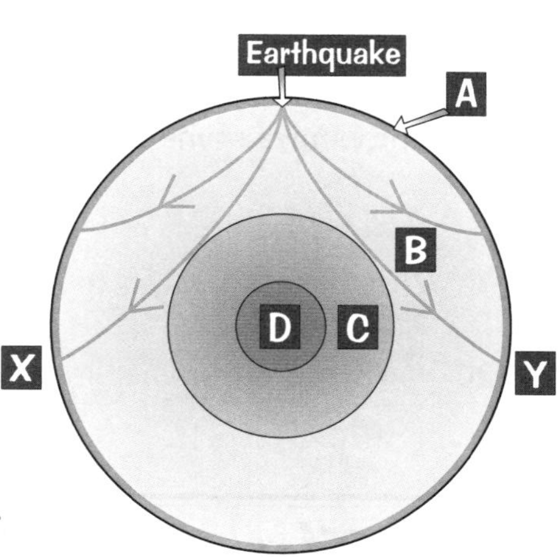


**Q13** Describe what an "**S–Wave**" is.

**Q14** What is the name for the region on the earth's surface beyond X and Y?

**Q15** Why are there no S-waves detected beyond X and Y?

**Q16** Describe the **state** of the rocks in layer B.

**Q17** *The paths of the S–Waves travelling through layer B are bent.*

**a)** What property of the rock in layer B is steadily changing, to account for this observation?

**b)** *Now compare this effect with the refraction of light waves.* Give **two reasons** why we can say that the S–Waves in layer B are **refracted**.

# Seismic Waves

**Q18** Give three ways in which P–Waves are different from S–Waves.

**Q19** *The diagram below shows the paths for some P–Waves travelling through the Earth.*

a) Point D is at the boundary of which two layers?

b) *The direction of the waves at D and E changes suddenly.* Why does this happen?

c) *Detectors are placed on the Earth's surface between points P and R.* Describe where you would not expect to detect any P–Waves.

d) What property do P-waves have that allows them to reach the parts other waves cannot reach?

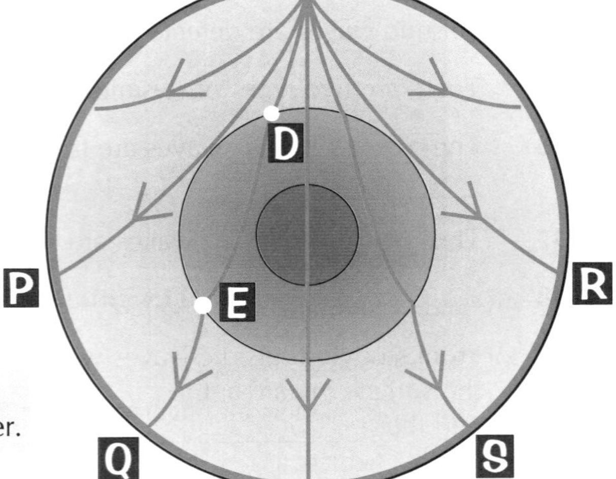


**Q20** After an earthquake, would you expect to feel the P–Wave first, or the S–Wave? Explain your answer.

The graph below shows how the velocity of a P–Wave and an S–Wave, travelling from the surface of the Earth towards the centre, changes with depth.

**Q21** Describe and explain **the shape** of the velocity–depth curve for **a P–Wave**. Say what is happening at A, B, C, D, E and F.

**Q22** Describe and explain the shape of the velocity–depth curve for **an S–Wave**. Say what is happening at A, B, C and D.

**Q23** Give **two reasons** why we should want to investigate the properties of the Earth's crust.

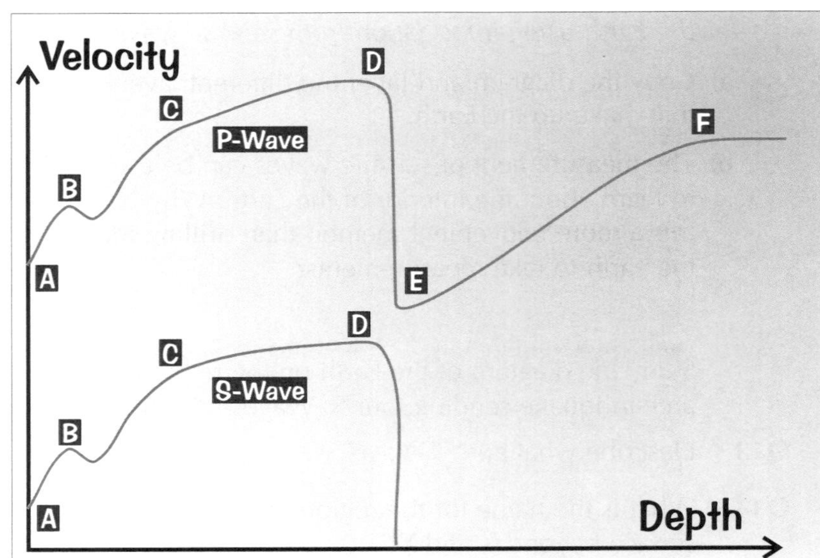


**Q24** Why do seismometers have to be placed deep underground, especially near towns and cities?

## Top Tip

If you know the basic facts on these pages you won't go far wrong. There are **two** kinds of seismic wave. The really important thing to remember is that **S** waves are tran**s**verse and they only travel in **s**olids, but **P** waves are longitudinal, and they travel through solids **and** liquids.

# The Solar System

**Q1** This question consists of a number of statements about our solar system.

For each statement, say whether it is **true or false**, and give a **reason** for your decision.

**a)** The Sun makes energy by changing hydrogen gas into water.

**b)** The inner planets all have similar surfaces.

**c)** All the planets are visible because of light they produce themselves.

**d)** The planets in the solar system orbit around a massive object.

**e)** Of the planets in the outer planet group, Pluto is an odd member.

**f)** All planets have spherical orbits.

**g)** Stars in other solar systems look dim because they are smaller than the Sun.

**Q2** The diagram below shows the outer planets of our Solar System.

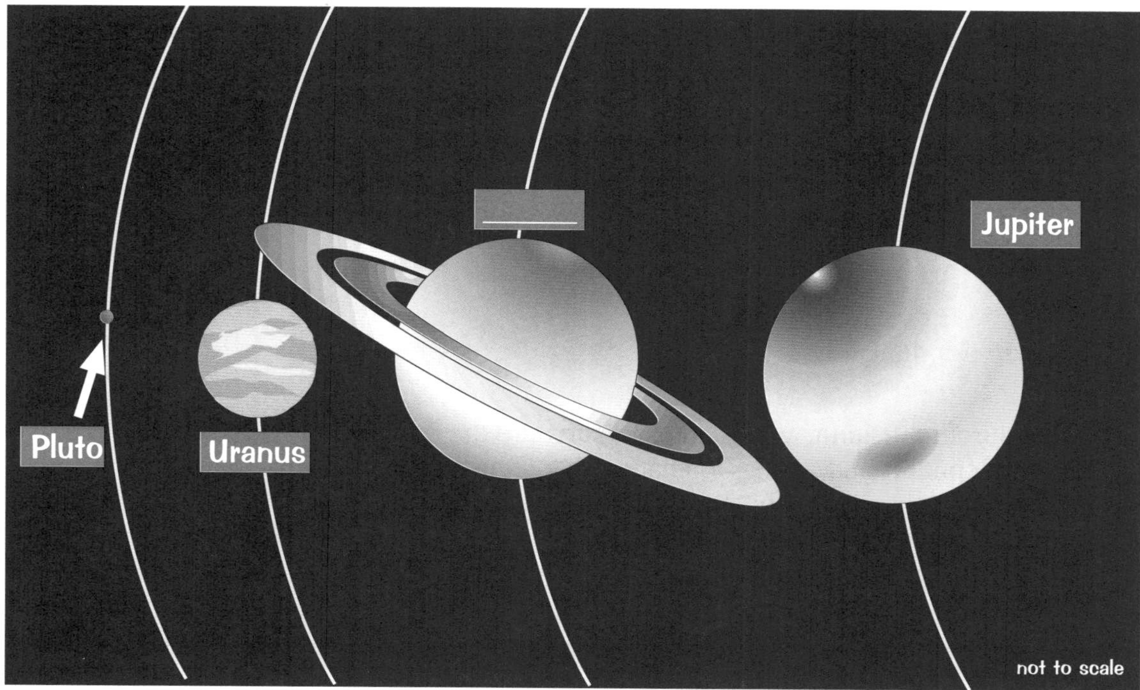


**a)** One planet's name has been left out. **Redraw the diagram** and add the missing name.

**b)** One planet has been missed from the diagram altogether. **Sketch in the orbit** on your diagram, and label it with the planet's name.

# The Solar System

**Q3** Jupiter and the Sun are both members of our Solar System.
The Sun is classified as a star, and Jupiter as a planet.

**a)** Complete the paragraph using the following words:

light, elliptical, huge, reflected, helium, heat, nuclear,

planet, fusion, stars, orbit, smaller, hydrogen, star

> The Sun is a ________ and produces ________ from ________ ________ reactions which turn ________ into ________. Like other ________ it is ________ and gives out a lot of ________. Jupiter, on the other hand, is a ________ hence the light we observe from it is ________. Jupiter is much ________ than the sun and follows an ________ ________ around it.

**b)** In your own words describe the characteristics that distinguish stars from planets.

(not to scale!)

**Q4** Viewed from the Earth, Venus and Mercury are the only planets that show phases and appear to change shape, just like the moon does. If we were on Saturn, which planets would show **phases**?

## Top Tips

You've got to learn the **order** of the planets (including the asteroids), so try a little silly sentence to help — My Very Elderly Mother etc., or something like that. The **differences** between **planets** and **stars** are pretty straightforward to learn, and a good way to some easy marks. Nothing to it, really.

# Moons, Meteorites, Asteroids, Comets

**Q1** **Look at the diagrams below** which represent photographs taken of a group of stars. The two photos were taken a few weeks apart.

An astronomer noticed that a planet had been captured on both photographs.

**a)** **Identify the planet** by putting a ring around it.

**b)** Why does a planet appear to cross the sky **relative** to the stars?

**c)** What is the **name** given to a pattern of stars that look fixed relative to one another?

**Q2** Most of the asteroids in the Solar System can be found between the orbits of two planets. Which two planets are these?

**Q3** Which two main substances are the asteroids made of?

**Q4** Some science fiction stories talk about a collision between an asteroid and the Earth. Why is this **extremely unlikely** to happen for most asteroids?

**Q5** An astronomer takes a timed exposure of the night sky with a camera that follows the stars.

***When she develops the film, she sees the stars as points, but there are also lines across it. These lines are not satellite or aircraft tracks, and there was no fault on the film. The photograph is shown on the right, here.***

What **astronomical event** could have caused the lines?

In Arizona there is a big crater in the desert. It was not formed by a volcano, but by some other natural event.

**Q6** How was the crater made?

**Q7** Why are there **very few** craters like this on the Earth, but **many thousands** of them on the Moon?

# Moons, Meteorites, Asteroids, Comets

Like all members of the Solar System, comets follow tracks around the Sun.

**Q8** What name is given to the **path** followed by a comet?

**Q9** Draw a diagram showing the **shape of the path** followed by a comet around the Sun.

**Q10** Give the **name of the shape** formed by the path of a comet.

**Q11** **Explain how** this shape differs from the paths followed by the planets.

**Q12** Comets are made from ice and rock. Their tails form as the ice melts and is left behind. Explain why a bright comet will fade with time as it completes more and more orbits of the Sun.

## Halley's Comet

*It was thought that comets were part of our atmosphere. However in 1577 AD, the Danish Astronomer Tycho Brahe proved that they were celestial bodies. The famous English astronomer Edmund Halley observed a bright comet in 1682, and concluded the same comet had appeared in 1607 and 1531. He predicted that the comet would return.*

**Q13** What value did Halley find for the **orbital period** of the comet?

**Q14** What **year** did he predict for the **next appearance** of the comet?

There are some comets in the solar system that have been trapped by the gravity of the planets. They orbit the Sun with periods of between 3.3 and 9 years.

**Q15** **Which planet** do you think will have had greatest gravitational effect on these comets?

**Q16** Will these comets be as bright as those with longer orbit times? **Explain** your reasoning.

***American space scientists have been designing missions to look at the larger asteroids, and maybe landing robots on them. If they are made from ice, then they would be a useful source of water for other space missions.***

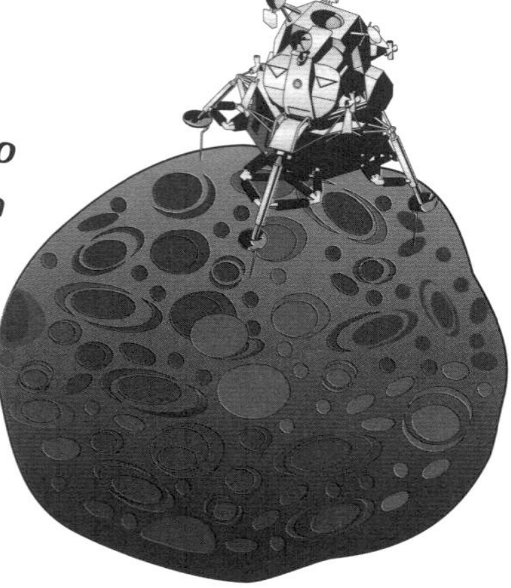

**Q17** **List** the difficulties a space mission to an asteroid would suffer from, compared with a mission to a planet like Mars.

## Top Tips

All the things on this page are really just **big chunks** of **rock** or **ice**, even the cool and exciting ones like comets and shooting stars. Don't let that dull your enthusiasm, though. You need to know about moons, asteroids, meteorites and comets, because they could ask you about them in the Exam.

# Satellites

**Q1** Artificial Satellites have been used for different purposes since the first successful launch in the 1950's. Today, satellites play an important role in our lives. The following statements can describe the motion of satellites.

*A. a high orbit*
*B. a low orbit*
*C. geosynchronous*
*D. move across the sky*
*E. above the atmosphere*
*F. in a polar orbit*
*G. in an equatorial orbit*
*H. orbits in a few hours*
*I. orbits in 24 hours*

**Which** of the statements above will apply to:

**a)** communications satellites?

**b)** most weather satellites?

**c)** spy satellites?

**d)** satellites broadcasting TV pictures?

**Q2** NASA has spent a lot of money putting the Hubble telescope into space.

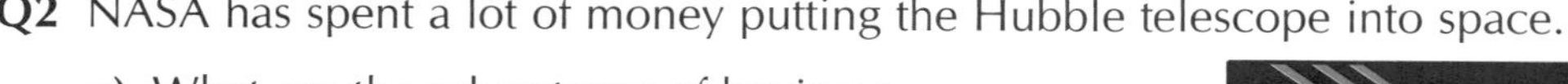

**a)** What are the advantages of having a telescope in space?

**b)** Why is this helpful to the scientists?

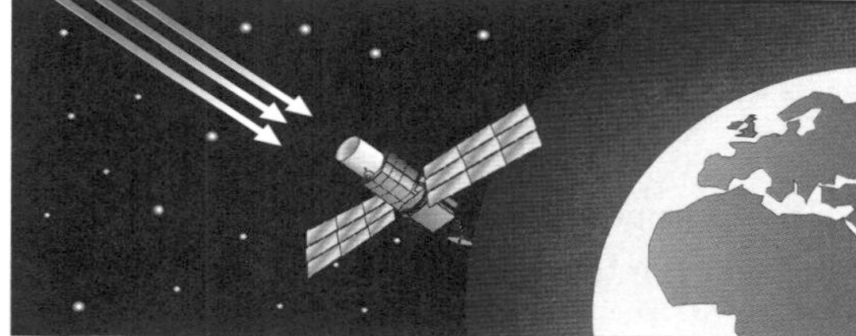

**Q3** If the space shuttle is in orbit, more than one Earth-based station is needed to communicate with it. Why would **one station** be no good?

**Q4** The Moon is smaller than the Earth. Its centre is situated 3.8 x 108 metres from the centre of the Earth.

**a)** Using the figures in the table below, calculate the gravitational field due to the Moon that we experience on the Earth's surface. (Recall how gravitational strength varies with distance.)

| | Surface field (N/kg) | Radius (km) |
|---|---|---|
| Earth | 9.8 | 6400 |
| Moon | 1.6 | 1600 |

**b)** **What effect** do seagoing folk experience due to this small field?

**c)** Consider a point on a straight line, $3.451 \times 10^8$m from Earth, between the Earth and the Moon. **What is the gravitational strength** due to the Earth at this point, to 2 significant figures? What is it due to the Moon? What is the overall effect of these forces?

## Top Tips

First of all, you need to know **why** people put satellites up there in the first place. Make sure you learn the difference between **geostationary** and **polar orbit** satellites — it's important, because you have to be able to say which **orbits** are used for which **purposes**. It's all there in question 1.

# The Universe

Q1 All the stars and galaxies that we see around us in the Universe today, started off in the distant past as huge clouds of gas and dust. These clouds collapsed to form what we see today.

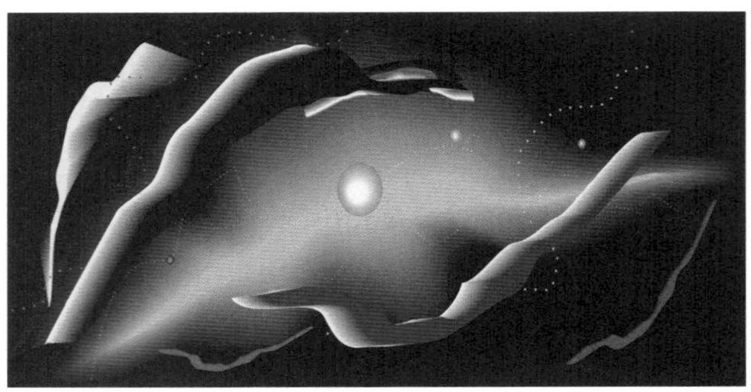

a) What caused the clouds to **collapse**?

b) As the clouds collapsed, nuclear fusion reactions began to occur within them. What caused these reactions to take place?

c) Explain what is believed to have happened when the nuclear reactions started.

The masses of some of the clouds were not large enough for nuclear reactions to begin when they collapsed.

d) Name **two** other things that may be formed when this occurs.

e) Why does everything we see in the Universe have a tendency **to rotate**?

Q2 Our Solar System is part of the Milky Way.

a) What is the Milky Way?

b) At night time, a milky white band can be seen stretching right across the sky. What characteristic of the Milky Way gives rise to this appearance?

Q3 Below are some facts about our Milky Way. For each one, decide whether it is **true** or **false**.

- [ ] a) Neighbouring stars in the Milky Way are usually much further apart than the planets in the Solar System.
- [ ] b) The Milky Way is about 10,000 light years across.
- [ ] c) The Milky Way is at the centre of the Universe.
- [ ] d) There are many known solar systems in the Milky Way.
- [ ] e) Our Solar System is at the centre of the Milky Way.
- [ ] f) The Milky Way has spiral arms.
- [ ] g) The stars we see at night are part of the Milky Way.
- [ ] h) The Milky Way takes a long time to rotate.
- [ ] i) The Milky Way is the biggest of its kind.
- [ ] j) The Milky Way is separated from its neighbours by lots of empty space.
- [ ] k) There are still gas clouds in the Milky Way.
- [ ] l) No more stars will form in the Milky Way.

# The Life Cycle of Stars

Astronomers have been studying groups of stars. They have used their observations to come up with an idea for how they think some of the stars evolved.

This "Life Cycle" is illustrated in the diagram below.

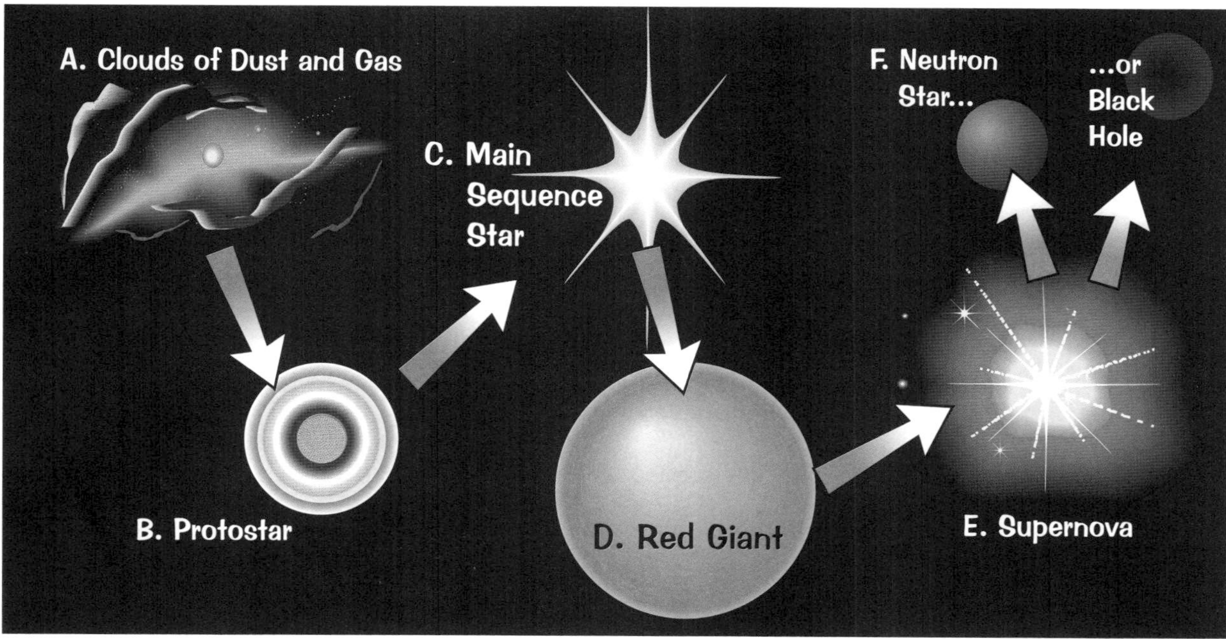


**Q1** What **type of star** follows this life cycle?

**Q2** Which type of star is our Sun?

**Q3** The scientists' ideas about stages A and B above are uncertain. Suggest why it is difficult to find **evidence** about these stages.

**Q4** At a certain stage in the life cycle, the temperature inside a star exerts an outward force. What **causes** the inward force?

**Q5** At which stage in the cycle do these forces balance each other?

**Q6** In the diagram above, many **heavier atoms** are made just before which stage?

**Q7** What is happening to make the red giant star **redder** than a main sequence star?

**Q8** How does the matter making up neutron stars and black holes **differ** from the matter we are used to on Earth?

**Q9** **Explain why** astronomers need to study a group of stars rather than just one or two, when studying life cycles.

**Q10** The first stars were formed from just two different elements. **Which elements are these**?

**Q11** What is the process in which **energy** can be created when atoms are forced together?

**Q12** Draw the life cycle for a small star (like our Sun).

# The Origin of the Universe

**Q1** We know quite a lot about the Universe and how it is changing.

Name and describe the **two main theories** that try to explain how the Universe began and continues to evolve?

**Q2** For each fact below, state which theory it could be explained by. (**Both** theories may apply)

**a)** The galaxies are all moving away from each other.

**b)** Galaxies have red shifts.

**c)** There seem to be galaxies in every direction.

**d)** Space is filled with a low frequency radiation coming from all directions.

**e)** Further away galaxies are moving away from us faster.

**Q3** When an object moves relative to an observer, the frequency of the electromagnetic radiation received by the observer changes.

**a)** What is the **name** of this effect?

**b)** What happens to the observed frequency if an object is **approaching**?

**c)** What happens to the observed frequency of an object that is **receding**?

**d)** **Give two examples** from everyday life of this effect in action.

**Q4** A lot of the observations of the Universe can be explained by the **Steady State Theory**, but scientists have two big problems with it.

**a)** What is observed that cannot easily be explained by the theory?

**b)** What is the **other problem** that scientists point out with the theory?

# The Origin of the Universe

**Q5** The picture below is a representation of part of a light wave emitted by a galaxy.

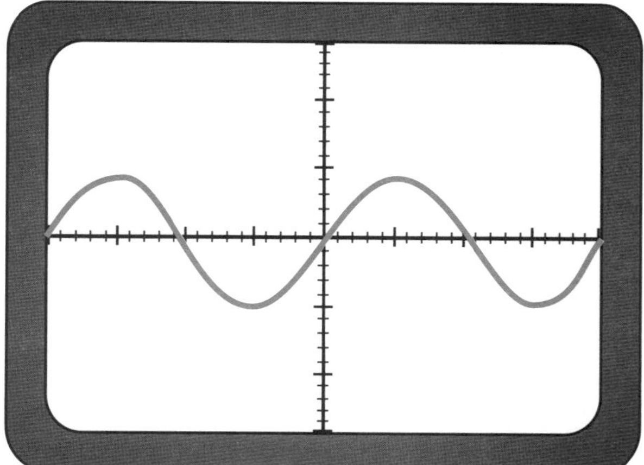

**a)** Copy the wave, and show how it is changed by the galaxy's movement **away from us**.

**b)** If the galaxy is replaced with a loudspeaker, describe what you would hear as it moves away with a gradually increasing velocity.

**c)** This change to the light waves emitted by galaxies has been happening throughout the Universe's history, and has been happening to the background radiation as well.
**What type** of radiation was the background radiation when the Universe was very, very, young?

**Q6** Some statements about the background radiation are given below.
Some are true, some are false. You have to **choose** which are which.

| True | False | | |
|---|---|---|---|
| ☐ | ☐ | **a)** | The background radiation has a low frequency. |
| ☐ | ☐ | **b)** | The background radiation is easily explained by the Steady State theory. |
| ☐ | ☐ | **c)** | The background radiation is coming from all directions. |
| ☐ | ☐ | **d)** | The background radiation comes from all parts of the Universe. |
| ☐ | ☐ | **e)** | The background radiation is ultra violet. |
| ☐ | ☐ | **f)** | The background radiation has changed since the Universe started. |
| ☐ | ☐ | **g)** | The background radiation was created well after the beginning of the Universe. |
| ☐ | ☐ | **h)** | The background radiation is microwave radiation. |
| ☐ | ☐ | **i)** | If we travelled to another part of the Universe, the background radiation would be the same. |

## Top Tips

These pages concern the **two** main **theories** about the beginning of the Universe and **how** we know what happened in the distant past. Scientists need evidence, and there are two important factors that you need to know about — the **red shift**, the fact that **far away** galaxies are **more** red-shifted, and the uniform background **radiation**. The **Big Bang** theory explains most of the evidence, so it's the most popular theory.

# The Future of the Universe

**Q1** Two factors help to determine how the Universe evolves.

**a)** What are these two factors?

**b)** One of them is **easy** to measure, one is a **lot more difficult**. Which is which?

**Q2** Measuring the total amount of mass in the Universe is not easy. Some matter is easy to see because it shines, and scientists can measure its mass. The rest is difficult, because we just cannot see it. For each of the objects below, choose which are **visible** and which are **invisible**.

*Supergiant Stars* *Interstellar Dust* *White Dwarf Stars*
*Black Holes* *Black Dwarves*
*Main Sequence Stars* *Dust between the Galaxies*

**Q3** The Universe is expanding. We can be sure about this much.

**a)** What is the **name of the force** that could be slowing down the rate of expansion?

**b)** **What causes** this force?

**c)** If there were no forces acting, how would the Universe continue to evolve?

**Q4** Scientists love drawing graphs to show what is happening in the Universe. **The graph below** shows what has happened to the size of the Universe up to now.

**a)** The curve on the graph opposite is not a straight line but rises less and less steeply. What does this tell us about the expansion of the Universe?

**b)** On two copies of this graph, sketch the two possible futures for how the Universe might evolve from now on.

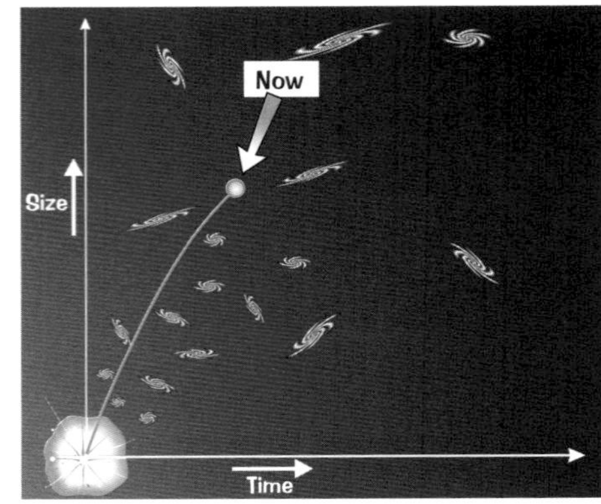


**Q5** Complete the paragraph using the following words:

*Universe, Solar System, 4.5 billion years, radioactivity, Universe, 2 billion years, Moon, Earth*

The first calculations made by scientists about the age of the ________ gave an age of only ________. This result was a big surprise because previous ________ measurements on rocks from the ________ (and later the ________) showed the age of the Solar System to be about ________. The ________ can't be older than the ________!!!

**Q6** The end of the world as we know it....

**a)** What is the "**Big Crunch**"?

**b)** **How long** (at least...) have we got before it occurs? (if it occurs...)

**Q7** Make another copy of the graph in Question 4. This time, extend it so that it illustrates a **cyclical Universe**; one that expands, then contracts, and then expands again.

# Energy Transfer

**Q1** What is the **significant** type of energy involved in each of the following?

**a)** A drawn longbow.

**b)** A red hot welder's rivet.

**c)** A mole of unstable uranium–235 atoms.

**d)** A piece of glowing magnesium.

**e)** A plate balancing on a pole.

**f)** A wire carrying a telephone conversation.

**g)** A high-calorie birthday cake.

**h)** A speeding bullet.

**Q2** In each of the following examples, energy is being changed from one type into another. In some cases, two or more types may be produced. State what the **changes** are for:

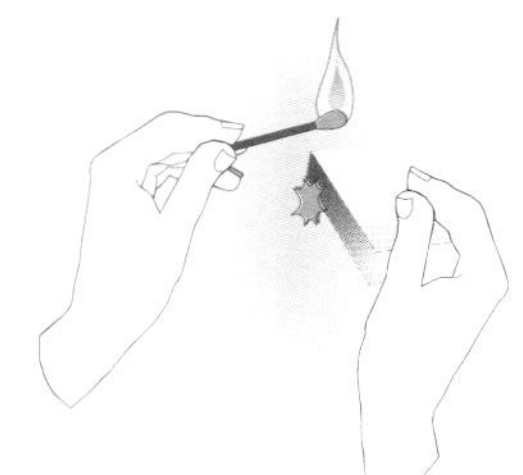

**a)** a descending rollercoaster car,

**b)** a crossbow bolt hitting a target,

**c)** a singer shouting into a microphone,

**d)** a cycle wheel spinning a dynamo,

**e)** a yo-yo climbing up its string,

**f)** a match being struck,

**g)** a magnifying glass concentrating the Sun's rays to burn a hole in a piece of paper,

**h)** a battery driving an analogue clock (one with hands),

**i)** a diver coming down on a springboard.

**Q3** In each of the following examples, energy is being changed from one type to another. **Work out** the missing energy types (there may be more than one in each case). For each one, name another object that performs the same energy change.

**a)** A radio changes ............................ energy to ....................... energy.

**b)** A match changes ........................... energy to ...................... energy.

**c)** A light bulb changes ......................... energy to ...................... energy.

**d)** A catapult changes ............................ energy to ...................... energy.

**e)** A hydroelectric dam changes ................ energy to ....................... energy.

**f)** An electric fire changes ...................... energy to ........................ energy.

**g)** An atomic bomb changes ...................... energy to ........................ energy.

**h)** A microphone changes .......................... energy to ........................ energy.

**i)** A car engine changes ............................. energy to ........................ energy.

**j)** A human body changes ............................. energy to ........................ energy.

# Conservation of Energy

**Q1** Copy and complete the following sentences which summarise the Principle of the Conservation of Energy:

> Energy can never be ________________ or ________________ .
> It is only ever ________________ from one form to another.

**Q2** Look at the energy flow diagram shown here. For each of the examples given below, draw an energy flow diagram. The first one has been done for you.

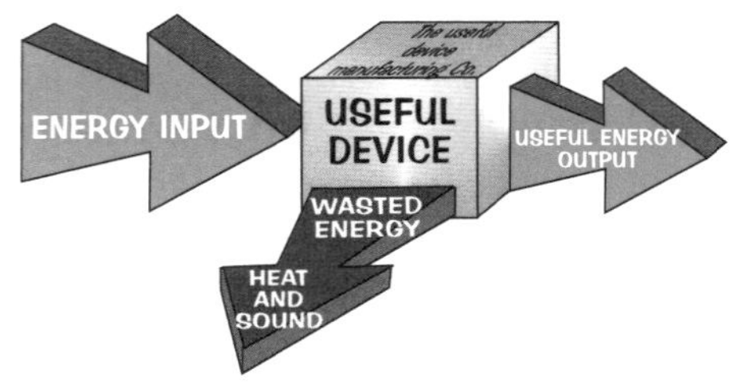


**a)** electric hoist.

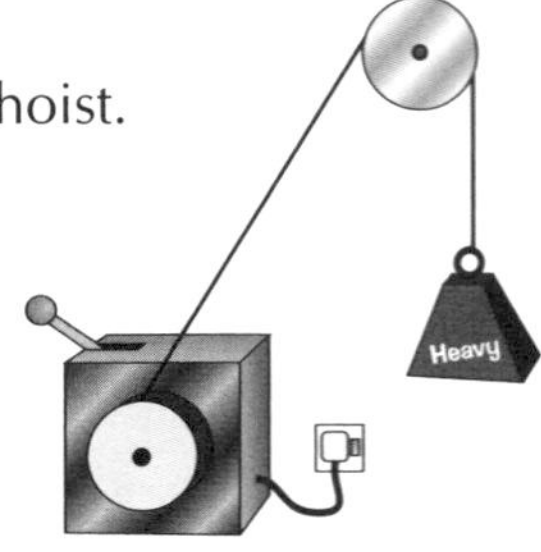


*Electric energy → HOIST → potential energy of load*
*↓*
*wasted sound and heat*

**b)** electric light bulb.

**c)** electric motor.

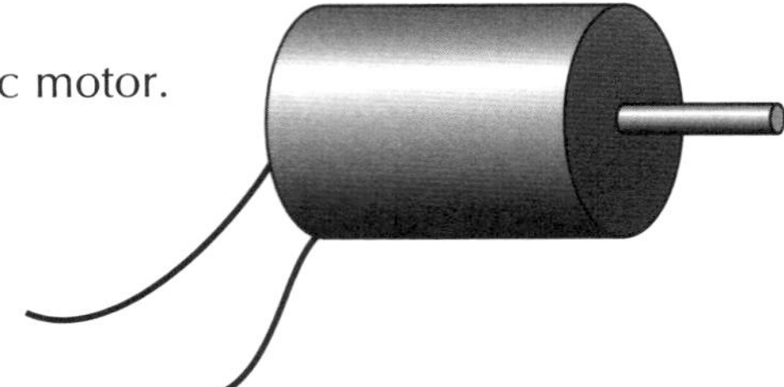

**d)** petrol-driven car.

**e)** electric kettle.

**f)** weightlifter lifting a weight.

**g)** solar cell for calculator.

**h)** computer monitor.

**i)** bicycle dynamo.

# Conservation of Energy

**Q3** In today's motor vehicles, lots of valuable chemical energy is changed to types of energy that are of no use to us at all.

**a)** What are these **useless** types of energy?

**b)** For each type, say **where** in the vehicle it is wasted (there may be more than one place).

Some engineers are busy trying to overcome the particular difficulties that trains and buses have when they are starting and stopping all the time. Every time they use the brakes, energy is changed to sound and heat which is then lost. It is suggested that as an alternative, the vehicle's energy is used to power-up a flywheel to slow it down.

**c)** What **form of energy** is a flywheel designed to gain?

**d)** What will happen to the **flywheel** as the vehicle slows down and transfers energy to it?

**Q4** Some people might say that wind power and hydroelectric power are examples of getting energy for nothing. **Are they correct**, and if not, **where** is the energy coming from?

**Q5** As you know, no energy transfer device is ever 100% efficient. This is because we cannot prevent the device from transferring the input energy into other, unwanted forms of energy. What are the two most common forms of **unwanted** energy produced by everyday appliances?

**Q6** An electric heater might be 100% efficient — the exception to the rule!

**a)** **Explain why** it can be considered to be 100% efficient. What could ruin the perfect score?

**b)** Is any energy **wasted** before it reaches the heater, and if so **where**?

## Top Tips:

When you think about all the energy wasted by motors and things like that, it's easy to forget that it all goes **somewhere** — it can't just disappear. The **total** energy is **always conserved** — you've just got to work out where it all goes. And if it doesn't add up to 100%, you've done something wrong.

# Energy Efficiency

**Q1** A student wants to find out about the efficiency of a stereo system rated at 20 watts sound output. She buys some batteries, which store 400,000 joules of chemical energy. When the new batteries are put into the stereo, and the machine is switched on to play a tape, the batteries are exhausted after 5 hours.

**a)** How much **energy** has the stereo **usefully** given out?

**b)** What is the **efficiency** of the tape recorder?

**c)** How would energy have been **wasted**?

**d)** If the stereo is used on the **radio setting**, would you expect the batteries to last longer? **Explain your answer**.

**Q2** A class of students is carrying out an experiment on a chemical rocket.

The rocket has a total mass of 2kg. They load the rocket with 3000 joules worth of fuel, of negligible weight. The class fire the rocket, and see that it rises vertically to a height of 100 metres, before falling back to Earth.

**a)** How much **potential energy** did the rocket have at its highest point?

**b)** What is the **efficiency** of the rocket motor?

**c)** How do you think **energy is lost** in the system?

**Q3** A handyman is using an electric sander with a rechargeable battery. He charges up the sander with 2500 joules of electrical energy. It should require 20 joules of energy to sand each $m^2$ of surface. At the end of three hours, the rechargeable battery is exhausted. He checks his work, and finds that he has actually covered an area of $100m^2$.

**a)** How much **useful energy** has gone into the sanding?

**b)** What is the **efficiency** of the machine?

**Q4** A company is asked to study the lift in an office building. They put different loads into the lift, and then study the electrical energy that the lift consumes lifting the loads up through a distance of 20m. The results of their experiment are shown below.

| Load (N) | Energy Consumed (J) | Energy gained by load (J) | Efficiency (%) |
|---|---|---|---|
| 1000 | 30000 | | |
| 1500 | 34000 | | |
| 2000 | 43400 | | |

**a)** **Copy and complete** the table.

**b)** What happens to the efficiency as the load **increases**?

**c)** **Explain** this pattern.

# Energy Efficiency

**Q5** A new design of electric kettle is supposed to be 96% efficient. It needs 200,000J of energy to raise the temperature of a kettle full of water from room temperature to boiling point.

**a)** How much **energy** will the kettle take from the **mains**?

**b)** What will the **rest** of the energy do?

**Q6** For a science project, Ashley is comparing a traditional light bulb with a low energy type.

Both the light bulbs give out the same amount of light.

The traditional light bulb is rated at 100W, lasts 2000 hours and costs 50p. The low energy bulb is rated at 20W and lasts 10000 hours — but it costs £9.50.

**a)** How much **energy** does each bulb consume in 10000 hours?

**b)** What would this **cost** if electricity were charged at 2p per MJ?

**c)** How much would the **bulbs themselves** cost for this length of time?

**d)** Which bulb works out **cheaper** in the long run? Explain your answer.

**e)** What **other considerations** might you make when buying a low energy bulb?

**Q7** My local garage uses a pulley system to lift the engine (weight = 3000N) up 1.5 metres from my car. It uses 6000 joules to do this.

**a)** How much potential energy is supplied to the engine?

**b)** What is the efficiency of the pulley system?

**c)** What effect would oiling the pulley system have on its efficiency? Explain.

**Q8** The manufacturers claim that an electric motor is 60% efficient. In an experiment, Sandra and Joan use it to lift a mass of 5kg through a distance of 1.20 metres.

**a)** How much **potential energy** is gained by the mass?

**b)** If the manufacturer's figures are correct, how much **energy** would you expect the motor to have used?

In fact, the motor actually consumes 110J.

**c)** What factors could the manufacturers say account for the discrepancy?

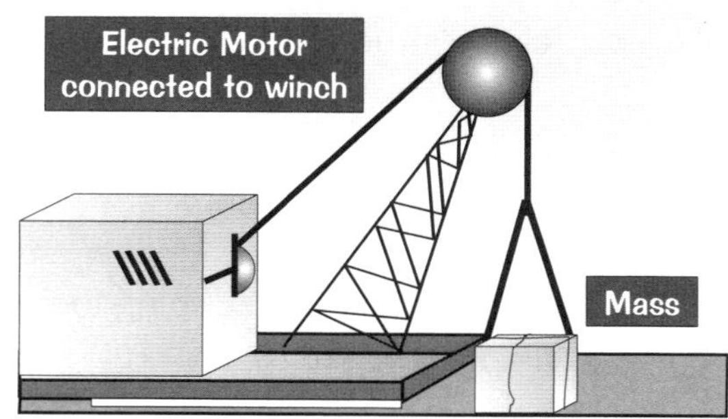


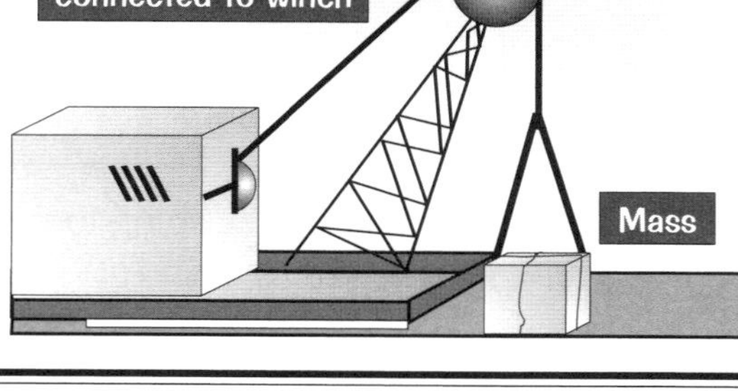

## Top Tips:

Energy efficiency — it's not just washing machines and light bulbs. But it is pretty simple — just one thing over another. If it comes out to more than **100%** then you've probably got it **upside down**. If not, it's probably right. All very simple, so just hope it comes up in your Exam, and easy marks will be yours.

# Work Done, Energy and Power

**Q1** Give 3 examples of **everyday sources** of energy that can be used to do **work**.

**Q2** Which of the following involve **mechanical work**?

**a)** A shelf holding up a stack of revision books.

**b)** A hamster moving a treadle wheel.

**c)** A footpump being pushed down.

**d)** A strong man leaning against a brick wall.

**e)** A weightlifter holding 40kg above her head.

**f)** A railway porter carrying a passenger's two cases.

**g)** The railway porter holding the two cases waiting for a tip.

**Q3** The table shows how the force exerted by a sprinter changes with the type of training shoe worn. It also records the distance moved by the sprinter in a time of 2 seconds.

**Make a copy** of the table and complete the final column showing the work done.

**a)** What **units** should be used for the work done column?

**b)** What **force** is the work mainly done against?

| Brand of trainer | Force (N) | Distance (m) | Work Done |
|---|---|---|---|
| Two Stripes | 4.2 | 1.6 | |
| Big Cross | 5.6 | 0.8 | |
| Off Balance | 4.8 | 1.2 | |
| Obverse | 5.9 | 1.4 | |
| High Vest | 4.5 | 0.9 | |

**Q4** My old car breaks down. Luckily the road is flat. There is a garage 1500 metres away. My car manual says it needs a minimum force of 700N to push the car along a flat road.

**a)** What is the **minimum energy** I will need to give the car to get it to the garage?

The car goes over a broken bottle, still 600m from the garage. A tyre bursts and the force of friction increases the required pushing force to 900N.

**b)** Calculate the **total energy consumption** in this case.

There is a slightly nearer garage. It is only 1300m away, but the last 100m are uphill, and the pushing force here would have to be 1150N.

**c)** Would I **save any energy** by pushing the car to this second garage, assuming that in both cases I avoid any broken bottles?

# Work Done, Energy and Power

**Q5** Scott and Sheila are waterskiing over a 400m course. When it's Scott's turn, a forcemeter on the tow rope registers a force of 475N. When Sheila has a go, the forcemeter registers 425N.

**a)** Calculate the **energy** needed to pull each skier over the course.

**b)** Why would the **total energy** consumed by the boat be **more** than this in each case?

Scott now starts to show off and puts in some turns. He manages to fit in 4 turns, each of 30m, but now only travels 320m in a straight line. During each turn, the forcemeter measures 520N.

**c)** Calculate the **energy** needed to pull Scott over the course in this case.

**Q6** A saw in a sawmill cuts wood into planks. The cutting of each plank uses up 2kJ of energy. When it is working at maximum power, the saw can divide 12 planks a minute.

**a)** **How much energy** is used by the saw in a **minute**?

**b)** Calculate the **maximum power** of the saw.

**Q7** Karl is fitting an electric motor to his radio-controlled car. The motor is rated at 50 Watts, and it can move the car along a straight track in a time of 5 seconds.

**a)** Assuming that the motor is 100% efficient, how much energy does the motor use up?

**b)** If Karl fitted a more powerful, 60 Watt motor to his car, how long would it now take to do the same amount of work?

**Q8** An electric kettle is rated at 2400 watts.

**a)** **How long** would it take to supply 288kJ to the water in the kettle?

**b)** In real life, the time needed would be longer than this. **Explain why**.

**Q9** James Watt was a pioneer of the steam engine. His steam engines took over from horse and water driven machinery, and the first machines had their power given in terms of horsepower. Given that Watt's "standard horse" could pull with a force of 500N whilst walking at 1.5 m/s, work out the **equivalent value in watts** for 1 horsepower.

**Q10** **Copy and complete** the following table which gives the results for some experiments carried out on a number of electric motors.

| Name of Motor | Work Done (J) | Time Taken | Power (W) |
|---|---|---|---|
| Fury | 150 | 30s | |
| Apollo | | 45s | 20 |
| Gemini | 300 | | 30 |
| Vostok | 4000 | 5 mins | |
| Soyuz | | 3 mins | 15 |

## Top Tips:

There's lots of calculations here, but nothing demanding. Just draw and remember the **energy efficiency equation**, and you're nearly there. Practice, that's the key to getting the **marks**. If you're still getting your energy inputs and outputs muddled — and your answers above 100% — then practise some more.

# Kinetic Energy and Potential Energy

**In the following questions, take g, the acceleration due to gravity, as $10m/s^2$.**

**Q1** Answer these questions on the basics of **kinetic energy**.

**a)** What is the **formula** for kinetic energy?

**b)** What do each of the terms in the equation **stand for**?

**c)** Give some examples of the **kinds** of objects that have kinetic energy?

**Q2** Some questions on **gravitational potential energy**.

**a)** What is the **formula** for gravitational potential energy?

**b)** What do each of the terms **stand for**?

**c)** Give some examples of the **kinds** of objects that gain or lose gravitational potential energy?

**Q3** This question consists of a list of statements **a)** to **h)**. Some are true and some are false. **Write down** which are true, and which are false.

| |
|---|
| **a)** If two objects are travelling at the same velocity, the one with the greater mass will have more kinetic energy. |
| **b)** Gravitational potential energy is the only type of potential energy in which scientists are interested. |
| **c)** Two objects of the same mass will always have the same kinetic energy. |
| **d)** If one object is double the height above ground than another with the same mass, it will have double the kinetic energy. |
| **e)** Kinetic energy is measured in joules. |
| **f)** The faster an object travels, the greater its potential energy. |
| **g)** The gravitational field strength, g, is important when working out kinetic energy. |
| **h)** If two different cans are on the same shelf, they will have the same gravitational potential energy. |

**Q4** The table below gives some figures for a car that is standing at traffic lights, and begins to accelerate away (at time, t = 0) once they have turned green.

| Time (s) | Velocity (m/s) | Kinetic Energy (J) |
|---|---|---|
| 0.0 | 0 | |
| 0.5 | 10 | |
| 1.0 | 30 | |
| 1.5 | | 2,662,875 |

The mass of the car is 2630kg. **Copy and complete** the table.

**Q5** Which of the following has most **kinetic energy**?

**a)** A cricket ball, mass 0.4kg travelling at 40m/s.

**b)** An athlete of mass 70kg jogging at 5m/s.

**c)** A cocker spaniel of mass 15kg running at 10m/s.

**d)** An industrial robot of mass 1000kg moving at 0.6m/s.

**e)** A bullet of mass 0.005kg travelling at 250m/s.

**Q6** A light aircraft is taking a group of parachutists up into the air. Dressed in her parachuting gear, Amy has a mass of 90kg. The aircraft takes the group up to a height of 5000m before they jump.

**a)** How much **gravitational potential** energy does Amy gain?

Amy jumps from the aircraft and free falls to a height of 3000m before opening her main parachute.

**b)** How much more gravitational potential energy does she have when this happens than when she started off on the ground?

The main parachute fails to open properly. Amy jettisons it — its mass is 5kg — and opens her reserve parachute.

**c)** How much gravitational potential energy does she have when she is 1500m above the ground?

# Kinetic Energy and Potential Energy

**Q7** A tourist's Fiat is driving along a mountain road. The combined mass of the car and luggage is 2920kg. The car is powering uphill at 23m/s.

a) **How much** kinetic energy does the car have?

At the top of the road, the car has gained a total height of 1200m.

b) **Calculate** the potential energy the car has gained.

As the car rounds a bend at the top of the mountain, a suitcase falls from the roof into the valley below. The suitcase has a mass of 20kg.

c) Work out the **potential energy** the suitcase lost when it had fallen a distance of 60m.

d) If all of this potential energy of the suitcase is converted into kinetic energy, **how fast** will it be travelling when it has fallen 60m?

e) Explain why it will not actually be travelling **as fast** as this.

**Q8** Some workmen are using a rope to lower a bucket full of bricks from a window. They tie off the rope when the bucket is just above the ground. As they are making their way downstairs to unload the bucket, a strong wind sets the bucket swinging.

Draw a diagram of the **path** of the swinging bucket. On your diagram:

**mark with the letter A** — where the **potential** energy is greatest.

**mark with the letter B** — where the **kinetic** energy is greatest.

**mark with the letter C** — where the bucket is travelling **fastest**.

**mark with the letter D** — where the bucket's **velocity** is zero.

**Q9** A bouncy ball has a mass of 0.3kg. It is dropped from a height of 3.0m.

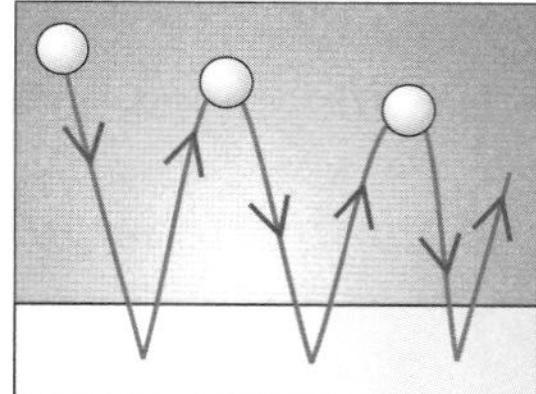

a) **How much** potential energy has the ball lost when it hits the ground?

b) Ignoring air resistance, **how fast** will the ball be travelling?

The ball rebounds vertically at a speed of 7.0m/s.

c) What **kinetic energy** does it now have?

d) What **height** will it reach on the rebound?

e) **Explain** what has happened to the energy that the ball has lost.

**Q10** Three students carry out an experiment to compare their own personal power. They measure their mass, then time how long it takes them to run up a flight of stairs 12m high. Their results are shown in the table below. **Copy and complete** the table.

| Name | Weight (N) | Time (s) | Potential Energy Gained (J) | Power (W) |
|---|---|---|---|---|
| Alex | 520 | 14 | | |
| Billie | 450 | 16 | | |
| Jack | 600 | 15 | | |

## Top Tips:

A lot of maths here, but it boils down to a couple of **simple equations**. The trickiest bit is knowing when to use them. Think about situations where both kinetic energy and potential energy are involved. For most, it's a pretty safe bet that if the PE's going down, the KE's going up at the same rate (and vice versa).

# Heat Transfer

**Q1** Below are a number of descriptions of heat transfer processes. State whether they are concerned with **conduction**, **convection**, **radiation** or **all three**.

- a) Heat flowing between two places when there is a **difference** in temperature.
- b) Heat passing from **atom to atom** (most effective in solid materials).
- c) Can occur through **transparent** substances.
- d) Sets up movement **currents** in liquids and gases.
- e) Is affected by **colour** and **shininess**.
- f) Can occur through a **vacuum**.
- g) Involves hot fluid **expanding** and **rising**.

**Q2** The paragraph that follows is all about **heat conduction**. You have to use the following words to fill in the **gaps**. The words may be used more than once or not at all:

**neighbouring collide carry reflect electrons pockets vibrate close good poor solids**

Conduction is the main form of heat transfer in ____________. This is because the particles are relatively ____________. Extra heat energy makes the particles ____________ more. They pass on the extra vibrational energy to ________________ particles. Metals are ____________ conductors of heat energy because they contain many free ____________ which can move through the solid and ____________ the energy. The electrons give up their energy when they ____________ with other particles.

**Q3** Write down three **insulating** substances and three **conducting** substances, then complete a table like this.

| Name of Substance | Conductor or Insulator | Used for |
|---|---|---|
| | | |

# Heat Transfer

**Q4** This diagram shows a metal bar with a number of holes drilled into it. The holes are just big enough to fit thermometers in. Four thermometers are put into the holes, and initially read the same temperature. The bar is then heated at one end with a Bunsen burner.

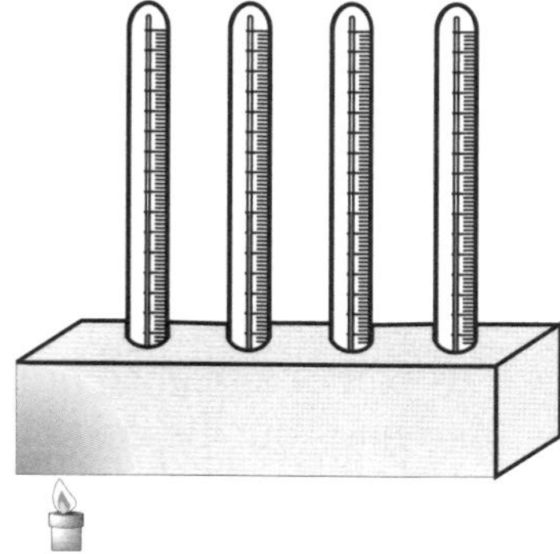

**a)** Redraw the diagram showing the **levels** recorded by the thermometers after a few minutes.

**b)** Explain the levels you have drawn.

**c)** Redraw the diagram showing the results if the same experiment was carried out using a bar of the same dimensions made from a poorer conductor.

**Q5** It's a hot day at the beach, and the only shelter from the Sun is behind an advertising hoarding. It is cooler where you are sitting, with your back against the hoarding, but your friend is still sweltering next to you. From your side, the board all looks the same colour.

**a)** What could be **causing** the difference?

**b)** You look out at the beach which is pretty deserted as it's so hot. You see a sunbed covered in white cloth with black plastic arms. There is a heat haze over the arms, but none over the cloth. Explain why.

**Q6** An author is planning to write an adventure novel.

**a)** The hero of the novel has to survive in the desert Sun having been tied up, in a car, by evil villains. Is he more likely to survive in a **light coloured** one or a **dark coloured** one?

**b)** Evening brings a new torture. The desert nights can be very cold. Which car will now be the most comfortable?

**Q7** Explain the following, using ideas of heat transfer.

**a)** Frosty nights in winter are usually **clear**.

**b)** In a hot water tank, the **heater** is generally at the **bottom**, and the **outlet** is usually at the **top**.

**c)** A layer of snow can **stop** young plants dying in the frost.

**d)** A shiny teapot keeps tea hot **longer** than a dull one.

**e)** Birds try to keep warm in winter by **ruffling** up their feathers.

**f)** Holding the legs of a transistor with pliers when it is being soldered can **prevent** heat damage to the transistor.

## Top Tips:

The main thing is the **three** methods of heat transfer. Get that sorted and you'll be ready for anything in the Exams. You need to be able to say **what's happening** in each type of transfer, and recognise the **situations** where they to occur. Don't forget, more than one type of heat transfer can happen at the same time.

# Keeping Buildings Warm

**Q1** Below is a list of methods of keeping heat within a house.

Describe how each saves heat energy, and give the type of heat transfer that the insulation method affects.

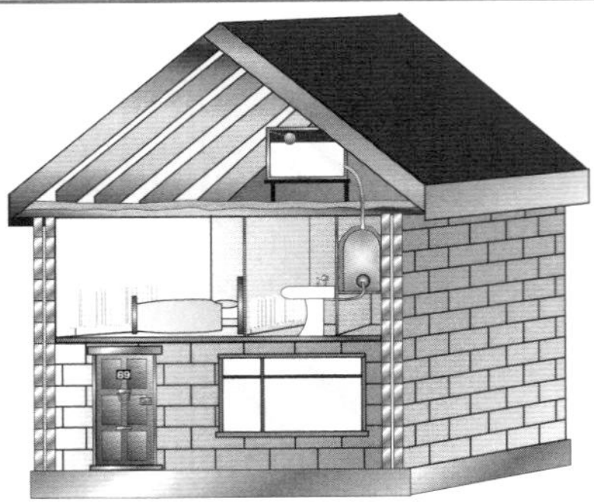

**a)** Curtains

**b)** Loft insulation

**c)** Cavity wall insulation

**d)** Hot water tank jacket

**e)** Double glazing

**f)** Draught-proofing

**g)** Thermostats

**Q2** As part of a science project, Eric investigates ways of saving energy in his grandmother's house, and finds out the cost of doing the work. Next, Eric calculates the annual saving that each piece of work would produce on his grandmother's fuel bill, as shown in the table below.

| Work needed | Annual saving (£) |
|---|---|
| Loft insulation | 40 |
| Hot water tank jacket | 15 |
| Double glazing | 60 |
| Draught proofing | 65 |
| Cavity wall insulation | 70 |
| Thermostatic controls | 25 |

**a)** Use the figures in the first table to draw a **bar chart**.

**b)** Which method of insulation makes the **greatest** annual saving?

**c)** Which method of insulation makes the **least** annual saving?

The next thing Eric does is to calculate the payback time, the time that each insulation method takes to save the money that it cost in the first place.

**d)** **Use Eric's figures** to construct a table showing **payback time** for each method.

**e)** Which method(s) of heat transfer pay for themselves **most quickly**?

**f)** Which is the **least** effective method when looked at in this way?

**g)** A double glazing salesperson calls and mentions some **other benefits** that double glazing would give. What **might** they be?

| Work needed | Cost of work (£) |
|---|---|
| Loft insulation | 250 |
| Hot water tank jacket | 15 |
| Double glazing | 3200 |
| Draught proofing | 70 |
| Cavity wall insulation | 560 |
| Thermostatic controls | 120 |

**Q3** A double glazing salesperson calls and gives you some figures. She says that the rate of heat loss through a single glazed window is 1.4 W/m$^2$ for each degree Celsius difference between the inside and outside of the pane. She claims that her double glazing can reduce that figure to 0.5 W/m$^2$.

**a)** Outside your house it is 5°C. Inside it is 22°C. How much energy is lost per second through each m$^2$ of **single** glazing? How much through each m$^2$ of **double** glazing?

**b)** What is the **energy loss per year** in each case? Assume the temperature difference remains the same throughout the year.

**c)** If you **heat** your house with energy costing 2p per MJ, how much would you save per m$^2$ in **one year** by changing your single glazing to double glazing?

**Q4** Sharon and Esme have booked a winter holiday in a log cabin. Sharon thinks that wood is a good substance to keep the holiday dwellers warm.

**a)** Do you agree?

They have a relaxing evening playing cards while it is cold and stormy outside. Esme goes up to the door. The body of the door is warm to the touch, but when she touches the brass handle, it feels very cold.

**b)** Explain **why** this is.

# Keeping Buildings Warm

**Q5** Sandra and her family have moved into a new house. They notice that the previous owners have taken away the insulating jacket surrounding the hot water tank in the airing cupboard.

The tank is a cylinder, 1 metre high with a diameter of 0.5 m.

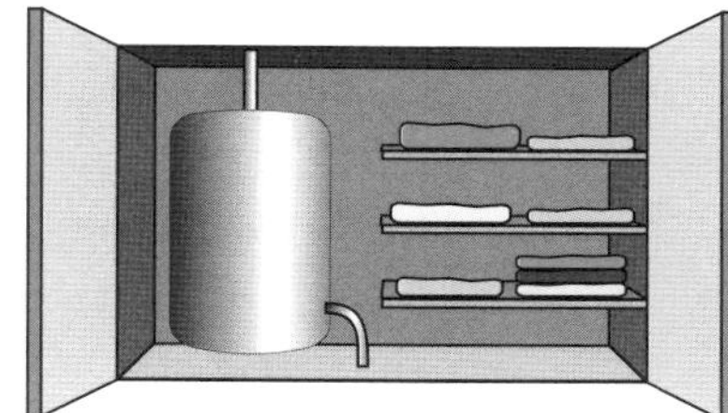

**a)** What is the **volume** of the tank?

**b)** What is the **surface area** of the tank?

Sandra's father suggests that instead of buying a new insulating jacket, they simply wrap the tank in shiny foil.

**c)** Which **method** of heat transfer will this reduce?

**d)** Is this likely to be effective on its own? **Explain**.

They decide that they will need a new insulating jacket. They want the water inside the tank to be at a temperature of 70°C. The temperature in the rest of the house will be 20°C. Sandra finds out that 1 kg of water gains or loses 4200J of energy when its temperature changes by 1°C.

**e)** Given that the density of water is 1000 kg/m$^3$, what **mass of water** does the tank contain?

**f)** How much **energy** would it take to heat up a tank full of water from 20°C to 70°C?

Sandra does an experiment on the tank. She heats the water to 70°C, and then switches off the power. An hour later the temperature is 68°C.

**g)** How much heat energy has the water **lost**?

**h)** What is the heat loss **per m$^2$** of tank surface?

**i)** What is the average rate of heat loss in **watts per m$^2$**?

Sandra goes to buy the insulating jacket, which has a thermal conductivity of 0.01W/m$^2$ per °C across it.

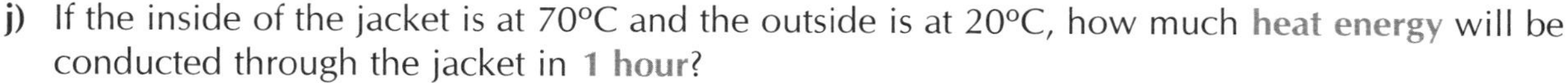

**j)** If the inside of the jacket is at 70°C and the outside is at 20°C, how much **heat energy** will be conducted through the jacket in **1 hour**?

**k)** If this energy is extracted from the water in the tank, what will the **temperature change** be?

**Q6** The vacuum flask has a number of features which help it to insulate its contents. Some features are listed below. For each of them, say **which method** of heat transfer they are reducing, and **how** they do this.

**a)** The cap is covered in **plastic**.

**b)** The cap is filled with **cork**.

**c)** The liquid is contained in a **glass** bottle.

**d)** The bottle is **double** walled.

**e)** There is a **vacuum** between the two walls of the glass bottle.

**f)** The **outside of the inner** glass layer is silvered.

**g)** The **inside of the outer** glass layer is silvered.

**h)** The bottle is surrounded by **air** inside the plastic case.

**i)** The bottle is supported away from the casing by insulating **foam**.

Outer cap/cup
Plastic cap filled with cork
Shiny mirrored surfaces
Vacuum
Sponge
Hot or cold liquid
Air
Plastic case

## Top Tips:

Examiners like asking you about these sorts of things — so make sure you know the functions of all the parts of the vacuum flask, and how **all** of the insulation methods work. Having an idea of the cost of each insulation method will help — and you need to know how "payback time" is calculated and used.

# Energy Resources

**Q1** Fill in the energy chains from the following list of words:

**Light energy, photosynthesis, plants / animals, clouds, light energy, heating sea water, heats atmosphere, rain, photosynthesis, light energy, plants /animals**

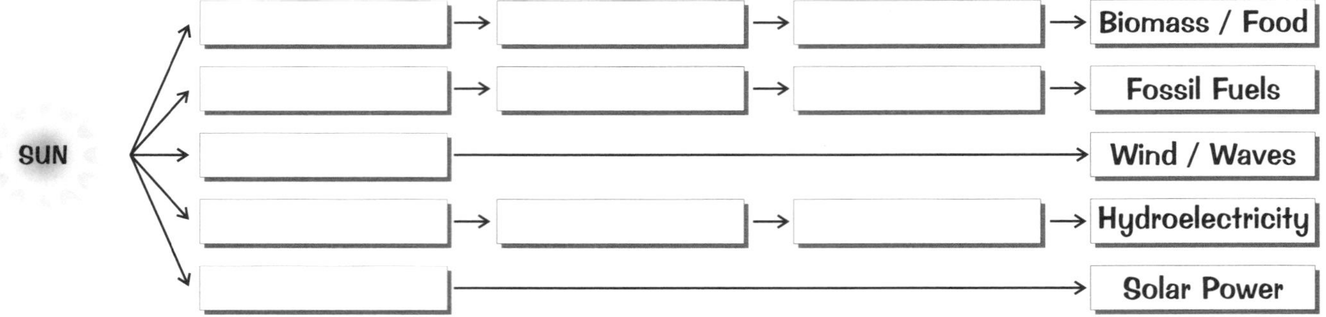


The Sun is the starting point for all of these energy chains.

a) What is the source of the Sun's energy?

b) How does the energy get from the Sun to the Earth?

**Q2** There are three energy sources that do not fit in with those from Q.1.

a) What are the three sources?

b) Which source uses energy emitted by the nuclei of some atoms?

c) Which source relies on the Earth's gravitational attraction to the Sun and Moon?

d) Which source relies on the decay of radioactive atoms within the Earth creating a source of heat?

**Q3** State the odd one out in each of the lists of energy resources below.
Give a reason for each of your choices.

a) Coal, Oil, Natural Gas, Nuclear

b) Wind, Wave, Geothermal, Solar

c) Tidal, Biomass, Hydroelectric, Geothermal, Nuclear

d) Food, Coal, Biomass, Hydroelectric, Oil

e) Nuclear, Coal, Geothermal, Oil

f) Solar, Biomass, Coal, Oil, Wave

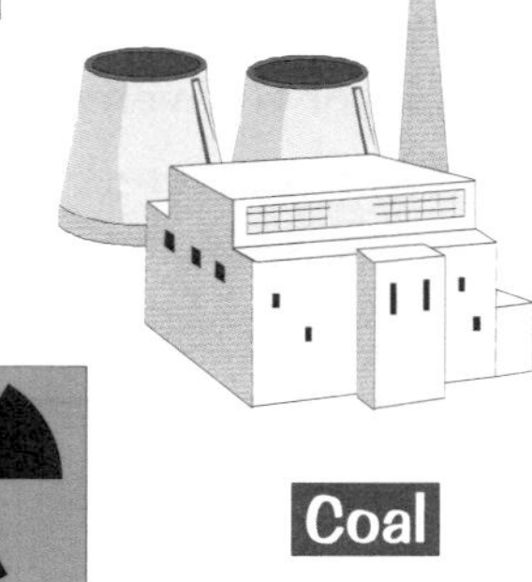

# Energy Resources

**Q4** When experiments were first carried out into nuclear power, it was thought that it would be a clean, safe and ideal energy source. However, we now know of at least 3 major disadvantages of using nuclear power to generate electricity.

Listed below are some of the arguments **for** nuclear power.
For each, list the **associated problems**, giving examples if you can.

**a)** Nuclear power generation is **clean**.

**b)** The uranium used to generate nuclear power is **cheap**.

**c)** We have the technology to generate nuclear power **safely**.

**Q5** Both geothermal energy and nuclear power rely on the energy locked up in the **nuclei of atoms**. What are the major **differences** in the way that the energy is produced?

**Q6** There are some people who say that coal, oil and natural gas are still being created on the Earth, and that they should not be regarded as non-renewable energy resources.

What is the main argument for still classifying them as **non-renewable**?

**Q7** The non-renewable energy resources are still being used to provide us with the majority of our energy. One thing that people are trying to plan for is a future when all of the non-renewable sources have been exhausted.

What is the other **major disadvantage** with our massive use of non-renewable energy resources?

**Q8** Coal, oil and natural gas can release their locked-up energy by combustion. This releases heat energy, which is converted to electrical energy in a power station.

**a)** What substance is needed from the atmosphere for this **combustion** to take place?

**b)** What two substances are **released** by the complete combustion of pure oil and natural gas?

**c)** Which of these substances **contributes** heavily to the **Greenhouse Effect**?

**d)** What do scientists think the Greenhouse Effect could lead to?

**e)** Where else in the **solar system** is a large Greenhouse Effect seen?

**f)** Coal and oil also contain **impurities**. What emissions can these give rise to when the fuels are burned?

**g)** What effects can this have on the **environment**?

## Top Tips:

There are 12 resources to learn your way around — 9 from Q1 (as there are 3 fossil fuels) and 3 from Q2. You need to know for each whether it's **renewable** or **non-renewable** — and make sure you know why. Also think about the **ultimate** source of the energy — like whether it comes from the Sun or not.

# Power Stations

**Q1** Despite scientific research into alternative sources of energy, most of the electricity that we use today is generated from 4 non-renewable energy sources.

**a)** Give the **names** of these 4 sources.

**b)** A traditional power station relies on the combustion of 3 of these sources. Which are the three that are **burned**?

**c)** Draw one simple **block diagram** to show the general structure of all 3 types of **traditional** power station.

**d)** Where will the **chemical** energy be changed into **heat** energy?

**e)** Where is the **heat** energy changed into **kinetic** energy?

**f)** What happens to **produce** the kinetic energy from the heat energy?

**g)** Where is the **kinetic** energy changed into energy of **rotation**?

**h)** Where is energy converted into **electrical** form?

**i)** How does the electrical energy get **from** the power station **to** the users?

**j)** **Draw** an energy chain showing how the energy types **change**.

**Q2** All of the non-renewable energy sources have associated environmental problems. On a **copy** of this table, put ticks to indicate which problems are associated with each source.

| Problem | Coal | Oil | Gas | Nuclear |
|---|---|---|---|---|
| Release of $CO_2$ contributing to Greenhouse Effect | | | | |
| Acid rain production | | | | |
| Devastation of landscape | | | | |
| Environmental problems due to spillage at sea | | | | |
| Expensive plant and clean-up after use | | | | |
| Production of dangerous, long-lasting waste | | | | |
| Danger of major catastrophe | | | | |

**Q3** Fossil fuels took **millions of years** to be formed. They are vital **chemical raw materials** and we just send them up in smoke. Our **man-made world** depends on fossil fuels. Give two examples of materials we would lose if fossil fuels ran out and suggest what alternatives we could use.

## Top Tips:

It's a good idea to be well up on the environmental problems associated with each of the forms of power production, as examiners are very keen on these. Learn the energy changes taking place at the different stages, not forgetting where energy is lost — and think about how fuel stocks can be conserved.

# Hydroelectric Power

**Q1** The Niagara Falls in North America are about 50 metres high. It is estimated that 1 × 108 kg of water pour over the falls every second.

If you could **design** a power station to extract half of the extra potential energy the water has at the top, what **power** would be generated?

**Q2** A power-generating company in the USA is trying to predict the power requirements for a city during an important sporting event that will be broadcast on TV. They are using figures from an event that was broadcast at an identical time last year.

The figures are shown in the table.

| Time | 19:00 | 19:30 | 20:00 | 20:30 | 21:00 | 21:30 | 22:00 | 22:30 |
|---|---|---|---|---|---|---|---|---|
| Power Usage (MW) | 23 | 28 | 35 | 50 | 36 | 34 | 65 | 26 |

a) Use the figures to **sketch a graph** of the power requirements against time.

b) At about what **time** did the event **finish**?

c) When was **half time**?

The company has 2 choices of how to deal with the surge in demand. It can switch on an extra boiler at their coal fired power station, or it can use their pumped storage station at the local reservoir.

d) Why would the coal-fired option be **wasteful**?

e) When would you advise the company to start running water **down** through the pumped storage power station?

f) When would it be best to pump water **back up** through it?

g) What would be the likely **energy source** for the pumping operation?

**Q3** This diagram shows a pumped storage reservoir system. The labels have been replaced with letters.

You have to **match up** the letters with the labels.

| turbines | |
|---|---|
| upper reservoir | |
| generator | |
| pump | |
| lower reservoir | |
| direction at night | |
| national grid | |
| direction during peak demand | |

**Q4** Put yourself in the position of a planner with a generating company, and decide which of the following points are advantages, disadvantages or **neither** when considering a location for a planned hydroelectric power scheme.

**a)** consistent and high rainfall.
**b)** high population in valley.
**c)** steep-sided valley.
**d)** remote location.
**e)** site of a rare species of plant.
**f)** nearby quarry.
**g)** rocks showing evidence of recent earthquake damage.

## Top Tips:

Hydroelectricity relies on the **potential energy** of water. Get used to the equation, and to converting energy into power. Pumped storage systems are big with examiners. Learn about their workings, and **why** they are so useful.

# Wind and Wave Power

**Q1** Copy and complete the following paragraph about extracting power from the wind, using the following.

increase remote high zero 5000 windmills
coasts large wind turbines noise moors blades
generator view

The energy of the wind can be extracted using devices called ____________, or more properly ____________ ____________. These can be situated in ____________ areas, such as ____________ and ____________ where there is a reliable history of wind. Each wind turbine contains its own ____________. The wind turns the ____________, providing the rotational energy needed to generate the electricity. Once the wind turbine is operating there is little material pollution, but people can complain about the ____________ and the spoiling of the ____________. In order to replace one coal-fired power station it would require about ____________ turbines, and this would cover a ____________ area of ground. Problems involved with wind generated electricity include ____________ initial costs, ____________ power being generated when the wind stops, and not having any way to ____________ supply when there is extra demand.

**Q2** The most recent design of wave generator uses the energy in water waves to drive a turbine and therefore generate electricity.

a) As waves travel towards the shore, what is the main direction of vibration of the water molecules?

b) How is this motion used to generate electricity?

c) What gives the waves this energy? What was its original source?

**Q3** The environments where these wave generators work are often quite hostile. Give some of the difficulties that the designers have to cope with.

**Q4** Once the wave generators are in place, there is little or no pollution of a chemical nature. However, as with any large-scale development, some people will be affected. Who are they and how are they likely to be affected?

**Q5** Wave generators are not very productive in very light wind conditions. They cannot therefore be counted on all the time. Researchers have suggested that the best place to put them would be where there was a long stretch of ocean over which the wind and waves can build up.

a) What would be the problems of siting the generators far offshore?

b) What other factors do you think might be a problem for wave generators in deep water?

## Top Tips:

Make sure you know your waves as well as your wave energy — including the effect of the wind. Think about what makes a good site for wave power. Learn about the disadvantages, too. Don't get wave power confused with tidal power — at least not if you want some marks in the Exam.

# Tidal Power

**Q1** At Rance in France, a tidal power station was completed in 1967. When the tide is in, a pool is formed behind the barrage. This has an area of $2.2 \times 10^6$ m$^2$. The barrage across the estuary contains 24 turbines which generate electricity as the water flows out to sea.

**a)** If the water behind the barrage rises an average of 8 metres after high tide, calculate the **volume** of water trapped by the barrage.

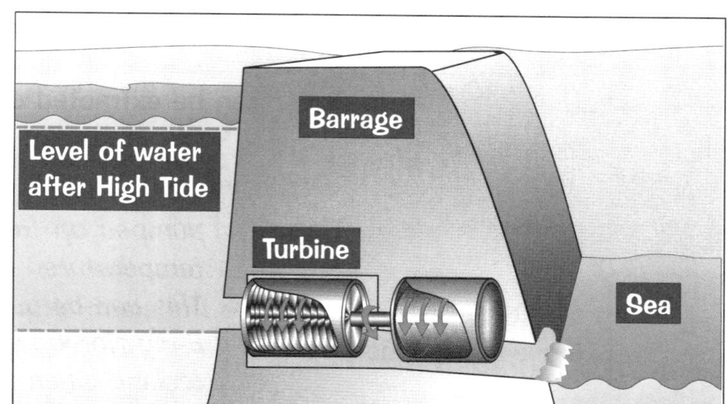


**b)** The density of sea water is 1030 kg/m$^3$. Calculate the **mass** of water trapped by the barrage.

**c)** If we assume that the water has gained an average height above low tide level of 4.0 m, calculate the **gravitational potential energy** that is represented here. (Take g = 10 m/s$^2$.)

**d)** If this amount of energy is released over 8 hours, what **power** does this represent, assuming that the turbines are 20% efficient?

Another possible site for a tidal station is the Bay of Fundy, in Canada. What makes this site especially attractive is the greater tidal range. Here it can be up to 18 m.

**e)** What **effect** will this have on the **generating power** of any tidal power station?

**Q2** In practice, the heights of tides vary throughout the month according to the relative positions of the Sun and Moon. **'Spring'** tides are when the variation between high and low tides is the greatest, while **'neap'** tides have the smallest variation.
What implications does this monthly cycle have for tidal power schemes?

**Q3** Tidal power stations are not only suitable for generating power on a regular basis, but they can also be used to **store energy** for periods of high demand.
Indicate roughly how you think that this could be done.

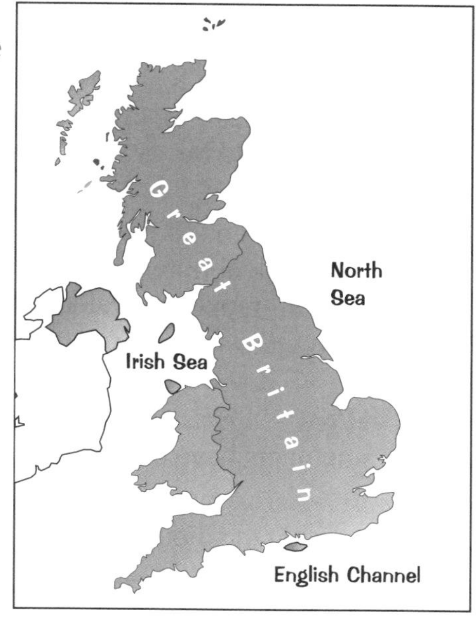


**Q4** Some people have said that about 100 tidal power stations, situated all around the coast of Britain, could generate the entire electricity needs of the country. What particular **drawbacks** can you see with this plan?

**Q5** At first sight, it looks like tidal power could be **energy from nothing**. Is this true? What will happen eventually?

**Q6** Many of the arguments against the siting of tidal power stations are concerned with their effects on people or the environment. **List** some of these arguments.

**Q7** Look at a map of the UK. Make a rough copy, marking some sites that might be **suitable** for a tidal barrage.

## Top Tips:

You've got to know the background details, like the cause of the tides. You'll need the **potential energy** equation, but don't forget that the average water rise **isn't** the difference between the tides. Think about other factors affecting tidal power — and why there are so **few** of these schemes around.

# Geothermal Power

**Q1** One of the places in the world where geothermal energy is being used to contribute to the overall energy needs is **Reykjavik** in Iceland.

a) What do you think makes Reykjavik **suitable** for a geothermal scheme?

Check out information on the plates that make up the Earth's surface.

b) **Why** are conditions this way in Iceland?

***In the city of Reykjavik, water can be pumped up from underground at varying temperatures between 95°C and 135°C. This can be used for direct heating of the houses. Early Norse settlers did exactly the same thing in Iceland when they first settled there.***

When the temperature of 1kg of water drops by 1°C, 4200 joules of heat energy are removed to the surroundings. In the 1970s, 16 boreholes supplied Reykjavik with 8000kg of water every minute.

c) If the water entered the system at 130°C, and left at a temperature of 30°C, **calculate** how much energy this represents over a 24 hour period.

d) How much power would be generated if all of this energy could be converted directly into electrical energy?

e) What could the water leaving the system at 30°C be **used** for?

**Q2** What makes an area suitable for geothermal power production?

**Q3** Why do geothermal sources have such a **long life**?

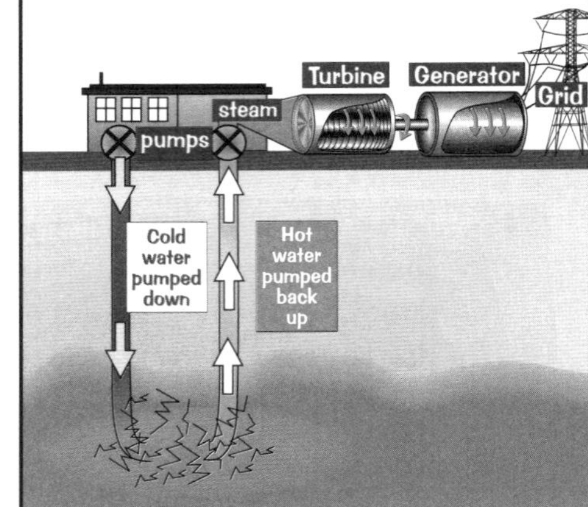


**Q4** One problem that may occur with water and/or steam that has originated below ground at high temperatures is purity. What could be the **cause and consequences** of this?

**Q5** When scientists investigate geothermal sources, they often talk about water at temperatures as high as 130°C. How can water remain at this temperature **without turning into steam**?

**Q6** What is the **major difficulty** that scientists and engineers have to deal with when planning and constructing a geothermal energy station?

**Q7** A site in the mountains of New Mexico, USA, was chosen by scientists. They drilled into dry rock and injected surface water. What **sort** of substance/structure were they hoping to find under the mountain?

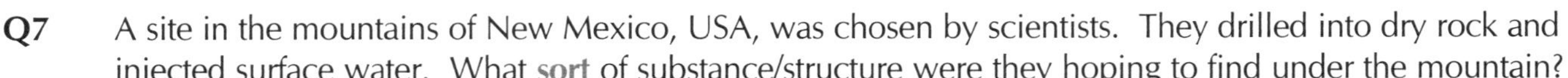

## Top Tips:

Geothermal power is brilliant, but it's only economical in some areas — make sure you know the factors affecting this. You need to know the main **drawbacks** and the costs, as well as the **source** of the energy. And looking at some plate tectonics stuff would be a good idea to help you get it all sorted in your mind.

# Biomass

**Q1** Put the stages in the generation of electricity from wood burning in their correct order.

| harvest trees | burn in power station furnace | cultivate fast-growing trees |
|---|---|---|
| produce steam | chop up trees | generate electricity | power turbine |

**Q2** Some scientists have worked out that, in the USA over 24 hours, the average amount of radiation falling on the land is about 180 W/m$^2$. If we take this figure, then how much energy falls on 1m$^2$ in **a)** 1 hour? **b)** 1 day? **c)** 1 year? **d)** 5 years?

**Q3** A bit of calculation can come up with the amount of energy falling on a forest of area 5km by 5km over a five year period. How much energy is this?

**Q4** However, trees don't convert all of the incident solar energy into chemical energy. They are not 100% efficient. Why else can't we take the figure above as the amount of useful chemical energy produced in the forest?

**Q5** A little more estimation can come up with an overall efficiency rate of 1% for the conversion of solar energy into chemical energy by trees. How much useful energy does this result in over the 5 years?

**Q6** If a wood-burning power station is 10% efficient, how long would a 1000 MW station take to burn the 5 years' worth of wood from our forest?

**Q7** How big a forest is needed to grow 5 years' worth of fuel for the power station in 5 years?

**Q8** What is the main conclusion about wood burning that these calculations show us?

**Q9** An environmental group has started up a campaign against plans to run a trial with a wood burning power scheme. They claim that the main product of burning the wood will be carbon dioxide, which will add significantly to the Greenhouse Effect. Is this a valid argument? Explain.

**Q10** The initial costs for setting up the scheme should not be too high. What will the costs be when the scheme is up and running?

**Q11** A shady local businessman claims that he can get hold of wood much cheaper from the rainforests in a developing country. He says that as you need wood, it doesn't matter where it comes from, and the developing country will be grateful for the money. What are the ecological arguments against taking him up on his offer?

**Q12** What could you do to try and convince those who say that huge forests of identical trees would be a real eyesore, and use up too much of the land?

**Q13** The burning of wood in the furnace would still lead to some of the problems associated with burning coal in more traditional power stations. What do you think they could be?

**Q14** There is another way that scientists have thought of using living organisms to harness energy from the Sun. Liquid or gaseous fuels, such as alcohol or methane, may be made.

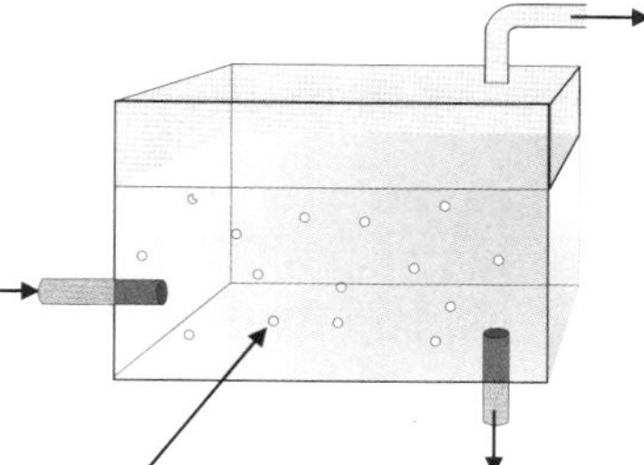

Look at the diagram, redraw it and add the labels from the box below.

## Top Tips:

Having a grasp of the sorts of figures involved in biomass schemes — like the sizes of the forests — would be a big help in Exams. Bear in mind that biomass doesn't *just* refer to the harvesting and burning of trees — you can use gas from rotting vegetation or sewage. Nice.

# Solar Energy

**Q1** **a)** What are the **three** different ways of harnessing solar energy shown below?

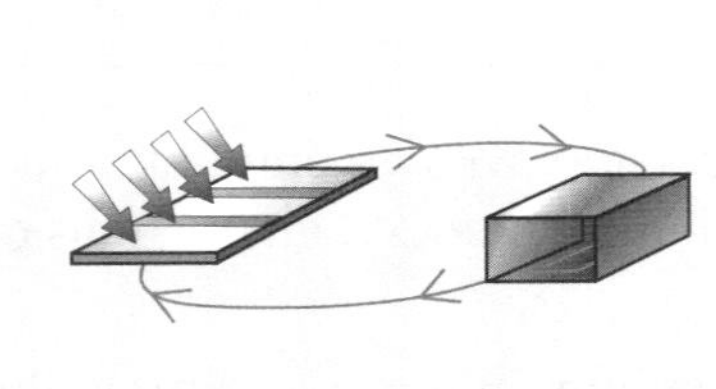

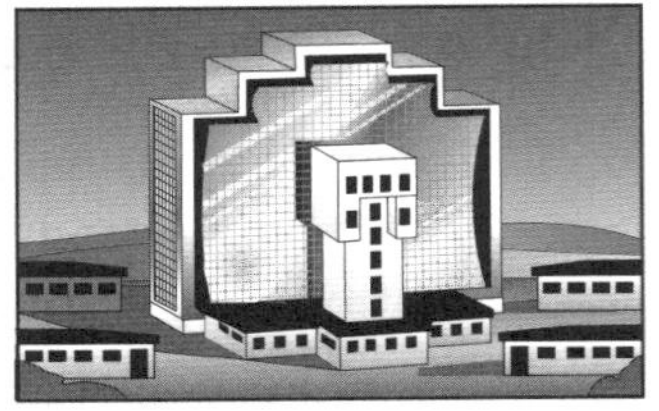

**b)** Here are a number of statements about solar energy.
Decide **which** of the three methods they apply to:

- **i)** The Sun's rays are **focused** onto one spot.
- **ii)** **Electric currents** are produced directly.
- **iii)** Curved mirrors **reflect** rays from the Sun.
- **iv)** A matt black surface **absorbs** solar radiation.
- **v)** Water is turned into **steam** to drive a turbine.
- **vi)** **Initial costs** are very high relative to output.
- **vii)** **Water pipes** feed in cold water and take away warmer water.
- **viii)** Extremely **high temperatures** are produced.

**Q2** A solar cell array is to be fitted to a satellite that is going to be launched into an orbit around the Earth. It's reckoned that the total solar power arriving in the region of the Earth is 1350 $W/m^2$. A new design of solar cell is 10% efficient. When the satellite is functioning fully, its power consumption will be 3.3kW.

**a)** Calculate the **area** of solar cells needed.

**b)** Will there be restrictions on when the satellite is able to be **fully operational**?

**c)** For a solar powered machine to operate at the Earth's surface, how would the area of cell array compare? **Explain.**

**Q3** An architect is designing a house that will rely on solar panels to heat some of the water for the central heating. He wants to use a <u>silver material</u> for the panels, as this will look futuristic. Explain why this is not a good colour for the panels, and tell him where exactly the panels should be placed.

**Q4** A local newspaper has started a campaign to get a solar furnace built in the UK. List some of the **disadvantages** there would be to locating such a power generator here.

## Top Tips:

There are **three** methods of **directly** using the Sun's energy here — so in your Exam you must be sure which one you're talking about. Learn **how** each one works, and what the **disadvantages** are. Think about our weather, and what use each of the methods would be in Britain.

# Atomic Structure and Isotopes

**Q1** The diagram opposite shows the particles that constitute an atom.

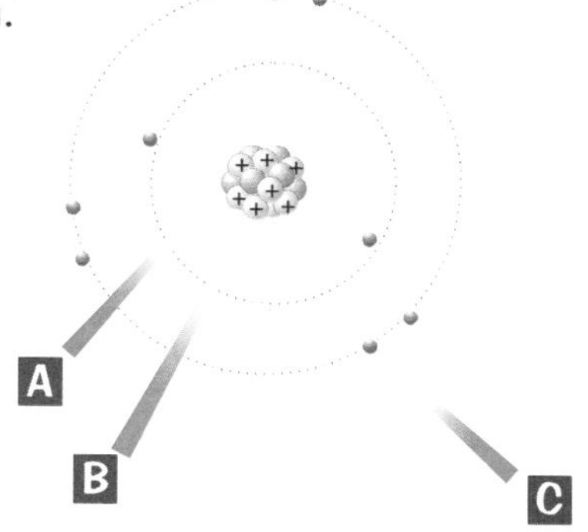


a) Name the particles labelled A, B and C.

b) What stops the electrons from flying away from the nucleus?

c) How many neutrons are there in the nucleus if there are 16 nucleons in this atom?

**Q2** The following paragraph describes the structure of an atom. Copy and complete.

All atoms consist of a ____________ and a number of ____________. The __________ is made up of ____________ and neutrons. ____________ have a positive charge and ___________ are electrically neutral. Most of the __________ of the atom is concentrated here but it takes up a relatively small ____________. The ___________ orbit the ___________. They carry a negative charge (and are really really _____________). The ratio of the mass of an electron to the mass of a proton or neutron is about ___________. The masses of the __________ and the proton are almost ____________.

**Q3** Complete the table opposite which summarises the relative mass and electrical charges of the sub-atomic particles.

| Particle | Relative Mass | Electric Charge |
|---|---|---|
| Proton | | |
| Neutron | | |
| Electron | | |

**Q4** The diagram below shows the apparatus used by Lord Rutherford to probe the structure of the atom.

a) Name the particles that are directed at the gold foil.

b) Why does this apparatus need to operate in a vacuum?

c) Which of the detectors measures the highest count rate?

d) Some particles are detected at Y. Explain this observation using your knowledge of atomic structure.

e) Just a very small fraction of the incident particles are scattered more than 90° by the foil (some of these are detected by detector Z). What does this tell you about the nuclei of the gold atoms?

Thin Gold Leaf
Source
Detector X
Detector Z
Detector Y

f) Gold was chosen as the target for this experiment. Give a reason for this choice.

g) Explain why a gaseous target would be unsuitable.

# Atomic Structure and Isotopes

**Q5** A stable atom of bismuth has a mass number of 209.

**a)** Explain what is meant by "**mass number**".

The atomic number of bismuth is 83.

**b)** Calculate the number of neutrons in the nucleus of a **stable** bismuth atom.

**c)** Describe how the structure of an **unstable** atom of bismuth will be different to a **stable** atom of bismuth.

**Q6** Copy the table opposite and **fill in the missing data**.

| | Number of electrons | Number of protons | Number of neutrons | Mass Number | Symbol |
|---|---|---|---|---|---|
| oxygen-16 | | 8 | | | $^{16}_{8}O$ |
| aluminium-27 | 13 | | | | |
| radium-226 | | 88 | | | |
| strontium-90 | 38 | | | | |
| hydrogen-3 | | 1 | | | |

**Q7** **Copy and complete** the following paragraph about isotopes using the given words. You may use a word more than once:

| | | | | | |
|---|---|---|---|---|---|
| atomic | mass | alpha | decay | neutrons | electrons |
| stable | beta | three | element | energy | protons |

Isotopes of the same ______________ have equal numbers of ___________ and __________ but different numbers of ______________. Hence they have the same ______________ number but a different __________ number.
Every ____________ has at least __________ different isotopes but usually only one or two ____________ ones. If a radioactive isotope decays, radiation is emitted. If an ____________ or a __________ particle is emitted then a different ____________ is formed.

**Q8** Information about six atoms A, B, C, D, E and F is given below.

| | |
|---|---|
| Atom A: 8 neutrons, mass number 16 | Atom D: 6 neutrons, mass number 11 |
| Atom B: 3 electrons, mass number 7 | Atom E: 3 neutrons, mass number 6 |
| Atom C: 8 protons, mass number 17 | Atom F: 6 protons, mass number 12 |

For which three atoms do you not need the mass number information to identify the element?

**Q9** Hydrogen has three different isotopes.

**a)** Write down the **common names** for these isotopes.

**b)** Which isotope is found in "**heavy water**"? Give a reason for the term "heavy water".

The three isotopes of hydrogen have identical chemical properties.

**c)** Give a reason why you might expect the **chemical properties** to be the same.

**d)** The boiling points of the three isotopes are different. **Explain** why.

## Top Tip

Just remember these definitions: MASS N$^{O.}$ = N$^{O.}$ OF PROTONS + N$^{O.}$ OF NEUTRONS and ATOMIC N$^{O.}$ = JUST N$^{O.}$ OF PROTONS (OR ELECTRONS). Isotopes of elements have different numbers of neutrons (so different mass number) but the same number of protons (so same atomic number).

# Three Types of Radiation

**Q1** The diagram below shows alpha, beta and gamma radiation being fired at a line of obstacles.

a) Copy the diagram.
For each particle, draw a line to show the path it travels before it is absorbed.

b) Give a reason why alpha particles only penetrate a short distance into a material.

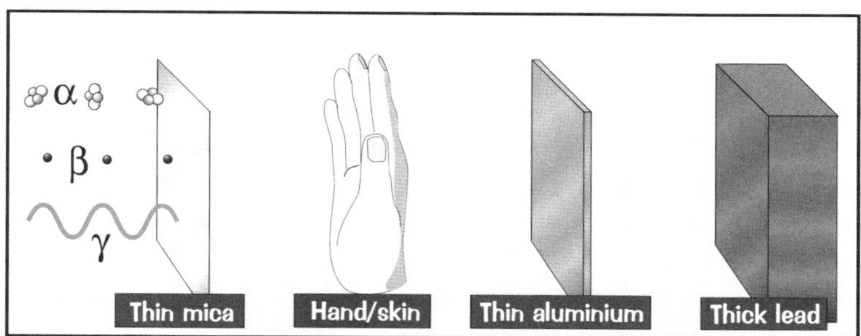


**Q2** The table lists some physical properties of alpha, beta and gamma radiation. The information has been mixed up.

Match each to the correct radiation.

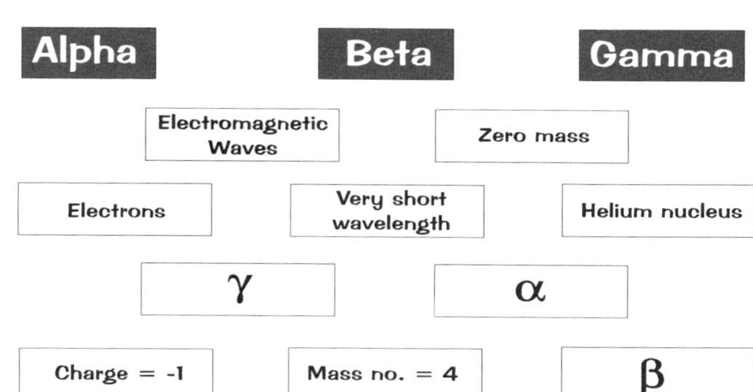


**Q3** For each question **a)** to **h)**, state which of alpha particles, beta particles and gamma radiation

a) has the largest mass?

b) travels at the speed of light?

c) causes the most ionisation?

d) has zero electrical charge?

e) is present in background radiation?

f) discharges a gold-leaf electroscope most rapidly?

g) is identical to a helium nucleus?

h) is an electron travelling at high speed?

**Q4** When radiation travels through matter it can cause ionisation.

a) Explain what is meant by the term "ionisation" ?

The diagram below shows a simplified drawing of an experiment to demonstrate that radiation can ionise matter.

The space between the plates is filled with argon gas at low pressure.
A current is measured.

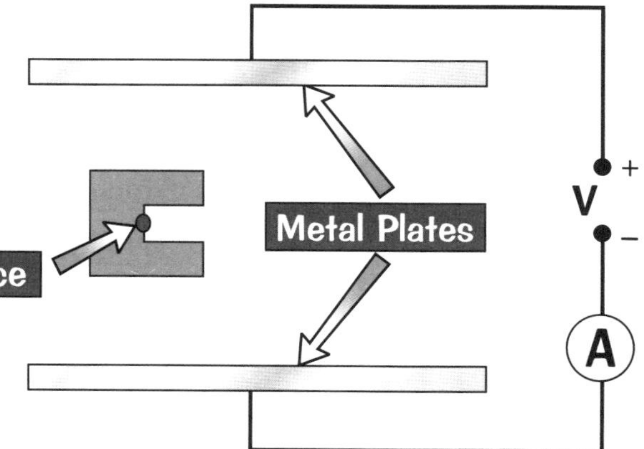


b) Name the two different particles formed when radiation from the source ionises an argon atom.

c) Describe how this leads to a current in the circuit.

d) The argon gas is removed from between the plates, leaving a vacuum behind. Explain why there is now no current flow.

# Radioactive Materials

**Q1** Radioactive iodine-131 is commonly used in medicine as a tracer.

**a)** Explain what you understand by the word "**tracer**".

**b)** Where will iodine-131 be concentrated if injected? Why is this?

**c)** What **type of radiation** is emitted by iodine-131?

**d)** Why would an alpha-emitting isotope be **unsuitable** for use in medicine as a tracer? Give **two** reasons.

**Q2** This question concerns the treatment of cancer using radiotherapy.

**a)** High doses of gamma rays can be used to treat cancers. What effect do gamma rays have on living cells?

**b)** **Explain** why a patient on a course of radiotherapy feels very ill.

**c)** For the treatment to be a success, what **two factors** does the radiotherapist need to consider before starting the treatment?

**Q3** Copy out the following paragraph and **fill in the gaps**.

irradiation dose surgical temperatures radioactive sterilise gamma instruments damage exposed microbes fresh safe emitter

A high dose of __________ radiation can be used to __________ food, keeping it __________ for longer. The process kills harmful __________, but does less __________ to food, as it doesn't involve exposure to high __________ like boiling. The food is not __________ afterwards, so it is perfectly __________ to eat. The isotope needs to be a very strong __________ of gamma rays. This method can also be used to sterilise __________ __________.

**Q4** After the sentences **a)** to **g)**, write down the **correct word or phrase** from this list below.

**Carbon-14 Heat Half-life Radioactive decay Chain reaction Uranium Electricity**

| | |
|---|---|
| **a)** Used as a nuclear fuel. | |
| **b)** Time taken for a sample's count rate to drop by one half. | |
| **c)** Energy is continuously generated in a nuclear fuel by a ... | |
| **d)** Useful for finding how long ago preserved plants and animals died. | |
| **e)** Radioactive decay always gives out energy in this form. | |
| **f)** Form of energy leaving a nuclear power station. | |
| **g)** Responsible for much of the heat inside the Earth. | |

# Radioactive Materials

**Q5** Look at the diagram below showing how the thickness of a metal sheet is kept constant by the use of a radiation source.

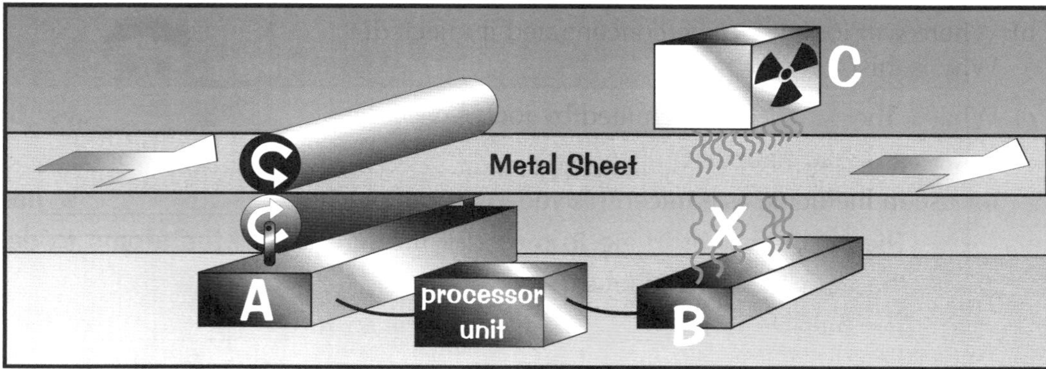


a) Name A, B and C. What **type of radiation** is X?

b) Suppose the thickness of the metal passing C **increases**. How does the system detect this change, and how does it return the thickness to its preset value?

c) The radioactive isotope used here must have a **long half-life**. Explain what would go wrong if the half-life was **only two hours**.

d) What **type of radiation** would you choose if you wanted to monitor the thickness of cardboard?

e) Explain why gamma radiation would be the **wrong** choice of radiation in **d)**.

**Q6** Gamma-emitting isotopes can be used to find out whether containers or pipes are leaking or not. An engineer wants to test an underground water pipe for leaks without digging up the road. It is buried one metre below the pavement.

a) **Describe** what the engineer would do to carry out his test.

b) The isotope needs to have a half-life of about a week. What problems could occur if it was much **longer** or **shorter** than this?

**Q7** **Copy** and **complete** the table summarising the uses of radioactive isotopes.

| Use of radioactive isotope | Alpha, beta or gamma emitter? | Short, medium or long half-life? | Reason for choosing short, medium or long half-life |
|---|---|---|---|
| Tracers in medicine | | | |
| Tracers in industry | | | |
| Sterilisation of food | | | |
| Thickness control (paper) | | | |
| Thickness control (metal sheets) | | | |

## Top Tip

You'll need to know at least three examples of where each radiation source is used (like the ones on these pages) — they're seriously easy marks. And you have to remember what the half-life of the source means and why that source is chosen. It all boils down to knowing your radiation.

# Half-Life

**Q1** Copy and complete the following sentences about the half-life of radioactive atoms.

zero long time half atoms radioactivity
gamma alpha beta short nucleus
decreases decay

The ____________ of a sample always ____________ over time. Each time a decay happens ____________, ____________ or ____________ radiation is emitted. This means a radioactive ____________ has decayed. The problem with trying to measure the time for all the atoms to decay is that the activity never reaches ____________.
The half-life is the ____________ taken for ____________ of the radioactive ____________ now present to ____________. An isotope with a ____________ half-life decays more quickly than an isotope with a ____________ half-life.

**Q2** Below is a table showing how the count rate decreases with time for a sample of polonium-218.

| Count rate in counts per second | 390 | 307 | 240 | 194 | 156 | 123 | 96 |
|---|---|---|---|---|---|---|---|
| Time in minutes | 0 | 1 | 2 | 3 | 4 | 5 | 6 |

a) Using the data in the table, plot a graph of count rate (vertical axis) against time (horizontal axis).

b) Using your graph, estimate the half-life of polonium-218.

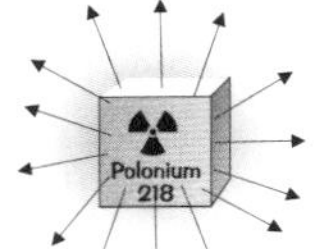


**Q3** A sample of a radioactive substance was found to be emitting 8000 beta particles a second at the beginning of an experiment. Fifteen minutes later, it was emitting 4000 beta particles a second.

a) What is the half-life of the radioactive substance?

b) How many minutes after the start would you expect to measure a count rate of 1000 particles per second?

c) What count rate would you expect to measure after two hours?

d) Background radiation from radioactive materials in the ground or in the air is about 2 counts per second.
How long would it take the count rate from the substance to fall below this background count?

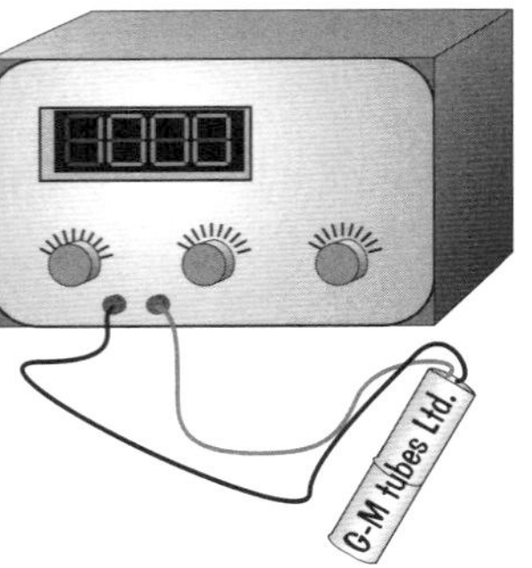


**Q4** The count rate from a radioactive material was measured using a G-M tube and counter. These are the results below:

| Count rate in counts per second | 95 | 73 | 55 | 42 | 32 | 23 | 18 |
|---|---|---|---|---|---|---|---|
| Time in seconds | 0 | 10 | 20 | 30 | 40 | 50 | 60 |

a) Plot a graph of count rate in counts / second (vertical axis) against time in seconds (horizontal axis).

b) Find the half-life of the material by finding how long it took the count rate to fall from 90 to 45.

c) Another material has a very low activity which makes it difficult to measure its activity above the background radiation. Describe how you might overcome this problem.

# Half-Life

**Q5** The half-life of carbon-14 is 5,600 years. Carbon-14 makes up about 1 part in 10,000,000 of the carbon in air. For each item in **a)** to **c)**, calculate **how long ago** it was living material.

**a)** A fossil containing 1 part in 320,000,000 carbon-14.

**b)** A spear handle containing 1 part in 80,000,000 carbon-14.

**c)** An axe handle containing 1 part in 20,000,000 carbon-14.

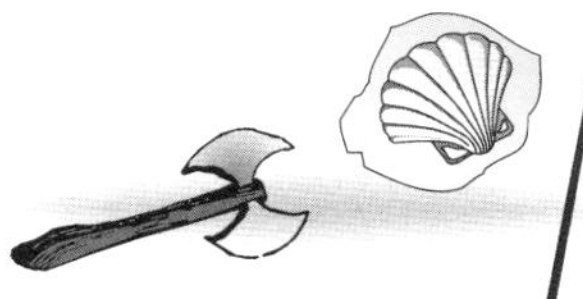

**Q6** **Fill in the gaps** in the paragraph below.

Carbon-14 makes up about one ten-____________ of the carbon in the air (carbon-____________ is the main isotope of carbon). This level stays fairly ____________ in the atmosphere. The same proportion of carbon-14 is also found in ____________ things. However, when they ____________, the carbon-14 is trapped and it gradually ____________ . By simply measuring the ____________ of carbon-14 found in the artifact, you can easily calculate how ____________ ago the item was ____________ material using the ____________ of 5,600 years.

**Q7** Igneous rocks can be dated if you measure the ratios of uranium-238 and its decay product lead. The half-life of uranium-238 is 4.5 billion years. Assuming no lead was present when the rocks were formed, **find the ages of the rocks** in **a)** to **d)** using the given ratios:

**a)** Uranium : lead is 1 : 1 **b)** Uranium : lead is 75 : 525

**c)** Uranium : lead is 1 : 0 **d)** Uranium : lead is 75 : 225

**Q8** Lead-210 (atomic number 82) decays with the emission of a beta particle. Bismuth-210 is formed, which decays with the emission of a beta-particle to form polonium-210.

**a)** **Draw** the above decay series, showing the mass and atomic numbers for all the atoms.

**b)** The graph opposite shows how the activity of bismuth–210 varies with time. **Estimate** the half-life of bismuth-210.

**c)** Polonium-210 decays with the emission of an **a**-particle. An isotope of lead is formed. What is the **mass number** of this isotope of lead?

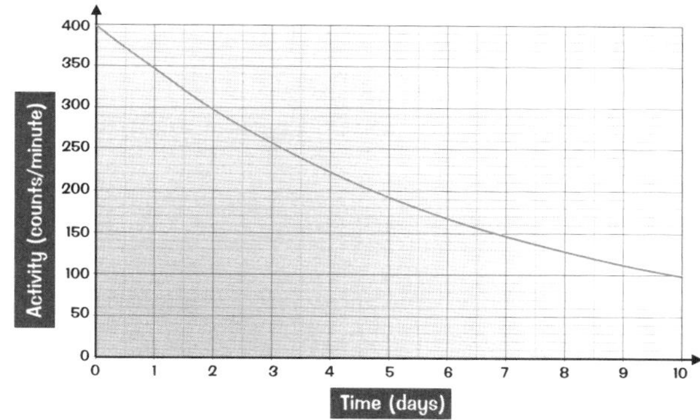


**Q9** The table below shows how the activity of a radioactive source changes with time. The background count rate was determined to be 10 counts per **minute**.

| Time(s) | 5 | 10 | 15 | 20 | 25 | 30 | 35 | 40 | 45 | 50 | 55 | 60 | 65 | 70 | 75 |
|---|---|---|---|---|---|---|---|---|---|---|---|---|---|---|---|
| Activity(counts/s) | 100 | 76 | 68 | 64 | 56 | 50 | 44 | 38 | 32 | 28 | 26 | 22 | 20 | 16 | 14 |

**a)** Use the data to **estimate the half-life** of the radioactive source.

**b)** The background radiation was measured over a long time. **Explain why** this is necessary.

## Top Tips

When a nucleus decays, it can give out alpha, beta or gamma radiation. **Half-life** is also **really important**. Radioactivity never completely dies away, but just keeps on halving. The **time taken** for it to drop by **half** is the **half-life**. Don't worry if you find the idea confusing, the questions are pretty straightforward.

# Radiation Hazards and Safety

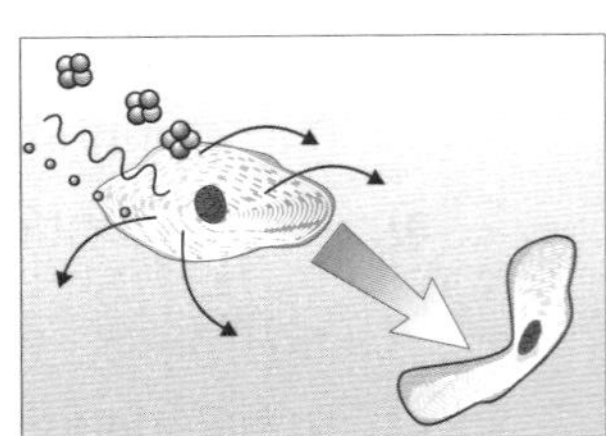

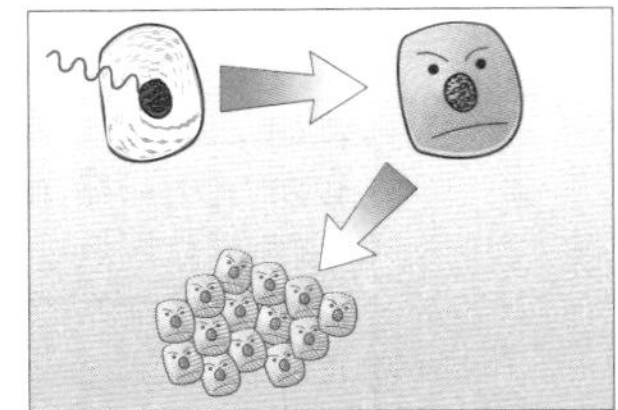

**Q1** Radioactive particles can be harmful to living cells.

a) Which **types of radiation** can do this damage?

b) What **process** usually has to happen for damage to occur?

c) Which part of the cell controls **cell function**?

d) What do we call a cell that has been **slightly altered**, but not killed?

e) Why are these cells so dangerous?

f) What do we call the **condition** commonly caused by these cells?

**Q2** Different types of radiation cause varying degrees of damage to cells.

a) Which of an **alpha particle**, a **beta particle** or a **gamma ray** is likely to cause the **most damage** to cells?

b) Why is this radiation more dangerous? Give **two reasons**.

**Q3** Radioactive particles can also give a person "radiation sickness".

a) How could a person develop radiation sickness?

b) What happens to the body to cause radiation sickness?

**Q4** List **at least three factors** which determine how much harm is done to a person when exposed to radiation.

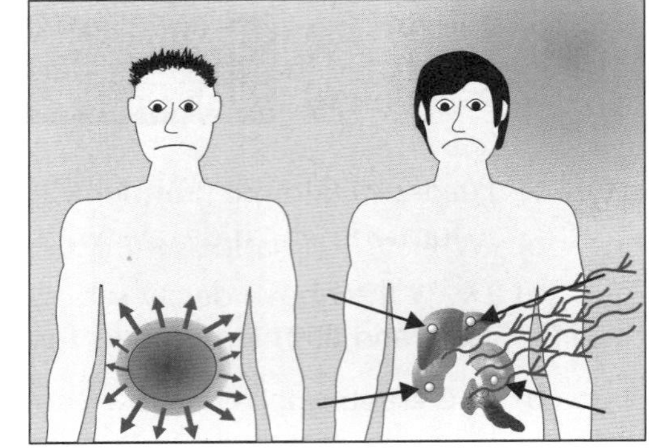

**Q5** Radiation outside the body —

What type(s) of radiation are most dangerous when **outside** the body? **Explain** your answer.

**Q6** Radiation inside the body —

What type(s) of radiation are most dangerous when **inside** the body? **Explain** your answer.

**Q7** There are rules to observe when handling radioactive materials in a school laboratory.

**Fill in** the gaps.

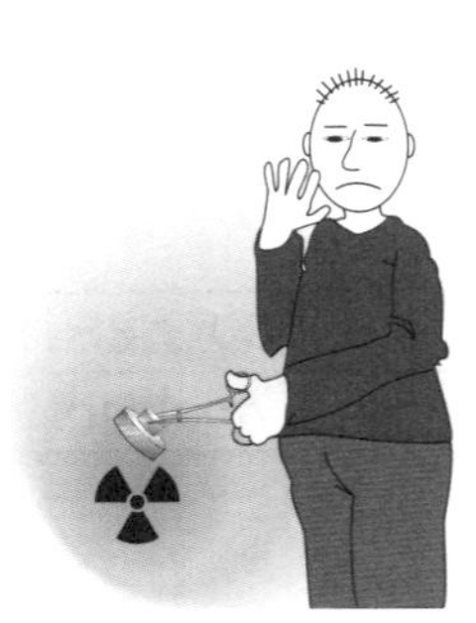

Never allow the source to come into contact with the _______________. _______________ should always be used to handle radioactive materials. Keep the source as _______________ the body as possible. Point the source _______________ _______________ the body. Avoid looking _______________ at the source. Keep the source in a box made from _______________ . When the experiment is finished, _______________ the source as soon as possible.

**Q8** People who work in the nuclear industry take even greater precautions.

**Describe precautions** workers can use to protect themselves from the following risks:

a) Tiny radioactive particles being inhaled or getting stuck on the skin.

b) Areas highly contaminated with gamma radiation.

c) Areas too dangerous even for the best-protected workers.

# Radiation Hazards and Safety

**Q9** The diagram shows a design for a smoke detector that could be fitted in a house. A weak radioactive source causes ionisation between the electrodes. The ions are attracted to one of the electrodes, and there is a small current.

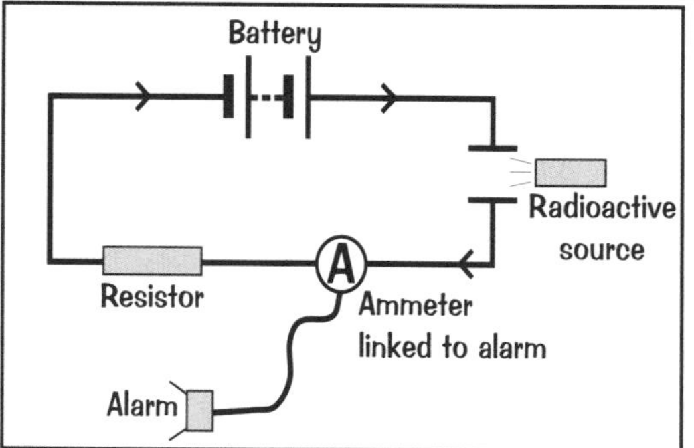

a) What **type of source** would be suitable for this application?

b) What happens when smoke enters the detector? How does this set off the alarm?

c) Some consumers might be worried about the presence of a radioactive source in the detector. How would you reassure them?

**Q10** In the Health Services, radiation is used in the treatment of many cancers.

a) What **type of radiation** is generally used?

b) What does the radiation do?

c) Why does the radiation need to be **very well-targeted**?

The medical physicists who are responsible for calculating the doses need to ensure that the dose of radiation is not too low or too high.

d) What could happen if the dose is **too low**?

e) What could happen if the dose is **too high**?

**Q11** A burn caused by radiation can look just like a normal burn, with redness and blistering around the affected area. However, radiation burns heal **a lot more slowly** than normal burns.

Why do you think this is?

**Q12** Young children and developing embryos are particularly susceptible to the effects of radiation.

Why is this?

**Q13** Bone marrow is important for white blood cell production and is easily damaged by radiation.

What effect do you think a **large dose** of radiation to the bone marrow would have on

a) white blood cell production.

b) the body as a whole.

**Q14** The Chernobyl power station disaster released (among other things), a cloud of radioactive iodine-131. Iodine is absorbed by the thyroid gland in the neck. People exposed to the radiation were given a course of **iodine tablets**.

— What were the authorities hoping to achieve by doing this?

## Top Tips

More great examples of radiation, which you WILL need, so add them to your brain-file. You already know that radiation can be dangerous but you need to **learn** all the **safety precautions**. I realise they aren't all that exciting, but they can ask you to list them in the Exam for some nice easy marks.

# Nuclear Equations

**Q1** Copy the table below and complete the information about alpha, beta and gamma radiation.

| Radiation | Mass Number | Atomic Number | Charge |
|---|---|---|---|
| alpha | | | |
| beta | | | |
| gamma | | | |

**Q2** How do the **mass number** and **atomic number** of a nucleus change, if it emits:

**a)** an alpha particle? **b)** a beta particle? **c)** gamma radiation?

(You might need to peek a periodic table for the next two questions.)

**Q3** The alpha decay of radium-226 is illustrated here.

The following nuclei, **a)** to **i)**, all decay by **alpha** emission.

**a)** Radium, $^{226}_{88}Ra$
**b)** Thorium, $^{232}_{90}Th$
**c)** Thorium, $^{228}_{90}Th$
**d)** Radium, $^{224}_{88}Ra$
**e)** Polonium, $^{216}_{84}Po$
**f)** Radon, $^{220}_{86}Rn$
**g)** Bismuth, $^{212}_{83}Bi$
**h)** Polonium, $^{212}_{84}Po$
**i)** Astatine, $^{217}_{85}At$

For each decay **write down** the symbol for the **daughter** nucleus.

**Q4** The beta decay of carbon-14 is illustrated here.

The following nuclei, **a)** to **i)**, all decay by **beta** emission.

**a)** Carbon, $^{14}_{6}C$
**b)** Uranium, $^{237}_{92}U$
**c)** Plutonium, $^{241}_{94}Pu$
**d)** Protoactinium, $^{233}_{91}Pa$
**e)** Bismuth, $^{213}_{83}Bi$
**f)** Lead, $^{209}_{82}Pb$
**g)** Thallium, $^{209}_{81}Tl$
**h)** Radium, $^{225}_{88}Ra$
**i)** Francium, $^{223}_{87}Fr$

For each decay write down the symbol for the **daughter** nucleus.

**Q5** For the following isotopes **a)** to **d)**, write down the **nuclear equation** representing the decay.

a) Thorium-234, $^{234}_{90}Th$, decays to form Palladium, $^{234}_{91}Pa$.

b) Thorium-230, $^{230}_{90}Th$, decays to form radium, $^{226}_{88}Ra$.

c) Palladium-234, $^{234}_{91}Pa$, decays to form uranium, $^{234}_{92}U$.

d) Thorium-232, $^{232}_{90}Th$, decays to form radium, $^{228}_{88}Ra$.

PHW42